"Cover Yourself Up,"

he said roughly.

Kara glared at him as she pulled the towel around her body.

Try to memorize what he looks like, she told herself, so you can give the police a good description. She had to admit he was handsome in a hard, ruthless sort of way.

"I'm here for a meeting with James Barnett tomorrow," he added. "He invited me to spend the night here."

"Well that's too bad," Kara shot back. "You'll just have to find other accommodations."

"We both know there are no other accommodations," he said harshly.

ALYSSA HOWARD
lives in Maryland and is a wife and mother, as well as a writer of fiction and nonfiction. She loves writing romances because they celebrate the most joyful part of a woman's life—and there's always a happy ending.

Dear Reader:

I'd like to take this opportunity to thank you for all your support and encouragement of Silhouette Romances.

Many of you write in regularly, telling us what you like best about Silhouette, which authors are your favorites. This is a tremendous help to us as we strive to publish the best contemporary romances possible.

All the romances from Silhouette Books are for you, so enjoy this book and the many stories to come. I hope you'll continue to share your thoughts with us, and invite you to write to us at the address below:

Karen Solem
Editor-in-Chief
Silhouette Books
P.O. Box 769
New York, N.Y. 10019

ALYSSA HOWARD
Love is Elected

Silhouette Romance

Published by Silhouette Books New York

America's Publisher of Contemporary Romance

SILHOUETTE BOOKS, a Simon & Schuster Division of
GULF & WESTERN CORPORATION
1230 Avenue of the Americas, New York, N.Y. 10020

ISBN: 0-671-57186-9

First Silhouette Books printing November, 1982

10 9 8 7 6 5 4 3 2 1

Map by Ray Lundgren

America's Publisher of Contemporary Romance

Printed in the U.S.A.

Love is
Elected

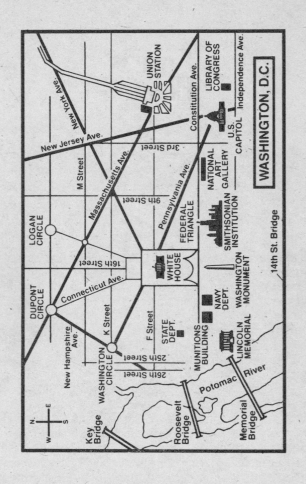

WASHINGTON, D.C.

Chapter One

Kara Barnett gripped the steering wheel tighter and squinted through the mist obscuring Highway 15. Towering shapes of tall pines loomed on either side of the country passage that led up the mountain to Uncle James' cabin.

Had she missed the turnoff? she wondered. She hoped not, because thunder was already rumbling in the distance and the sky had taken on an ominous cast.

Getting caught in a spring storm would be a fitting end to a wretched day, Kara assured herself grimly. First there had been the fiasco at work. As public relations specialist at Citizens for Consumer Protection in Washington, D.C., Kara had spent the last two months lobbying for stricter toy safety inspection regulations. But she'd found out this morning that the bill she was pushing was stuck in committee.

With Congress adjourning for a three week break, there wasn't a prayer of passing it this session.

Then there had been the humiliating call from Wayne Lyle—the handsome lawyer Kara had been dating for half a year, almost ever since she'd come to D.C. with her B.A. in public relations tucked under her arm. For the past several months he'd been pressing his own campaign—trying to get her to move out of the apartment she shared in Georgetown with Jill Sanders and into his Roslyn highrise. But recently he'd slackened the pressure. And she had breathed a sigh of relief, until this afternoon, when he'd called to tell her he wouldn't be seeing her anymore because Gloria Ferguson was moving in with him.

That bleached-blond pushover, Kara fumed. She may be more glamorous than I am, but I thought that wasn't important. Kara glanced critically in the mirror, inspecting her own dark curls, heart-shaped face and wide violet eyes, totally unaware of their potential for real beauty. Had she been wrong, Kara wondered, to turn down Wayne's proposition? He had called her old-fashioned.

"But that's just the way I am," she muttered fiercely to herself as she clutched the wheel tighter. I want a special man to share the rest of my life, to make a home with and raise a family, and not just an affair that lasts a few months. I'm not going to move in with any man unless we're married!

Kara reflected back over the past few months, remembering a time when she had thought Wayne might be that man. Getting the big rush from him had been a heady experience at first. It had come at a time when she had been ready for love.

Kara's parents had been killed six years ago in a plane crash, and she had spent most of her life since then in fancy boarding schools, summer camps, and a girls' college where there were few eligible men to date. She had grown self-sufficient and independent in those years, but she had been starved for affection. She had been eager to soak up the flattering attention Wayne had lavished on her.

But after a few months, something in her had reluctantly pulled back. She had begun to suspect that Wayne's plans for her didn't include wedding bells. Yet she couldn't help clinging to the hope that she could make their relationship into what she wanted it to be. And there was no doubt about it—despite her suspicions that it might be coming, his rejection had hurt terribly.

Her roommate Jill had tried to be consoling. But Kara didn't want anyone's sympathy. She wanted to be alone to sort out her feelings. So she'd packed an overnight case, left D.C. in the height of rush-hour traffic, and headed for Uncle James' cabin in rural Frederick County. Along the way she had stopped for enough groceries to last through the weekend.

Suddenly Kara slammed on the brakes. She'd been so involved in her thoughts that she had overshot the dirt turnoff to the cabin. After backing up and shifting down, she nosed her yellow hatchback onto the rutted drive. Large drops of rain were just beginning to plop against the windshield.

Kara stopped the car in the clearing beside the cabin. Just as she turned off the ignition, the skies opened up. Sheets of rain began to pelt against the sturdy A-frame that Uncle James had built as a getaway when he was still Party Chairman.

James was her father's older brother. And for the thousandth time she wondered why he, and not her parents, had walked away from that company plane wreck. But then he had always been the lucky one.

For the past six years—out of what she surmised was a sense of duty—he'd been her guardian, paying her bills at school and camp. But when she'd been at his house during vacations, he'd always seemed too busy, too wrapped up in his political wheeling and dealing to take much interest in her.

There had always been expensive presents like giant stuffed animals, a room full of French Provincial furniture and fancy stereo equipment. But for Kara, none of these made up for the fact that he was never at home for dinner.

She'd forced herself to be independent, but when she'd graduated from college and gotten a job, she'd still been hurt at his seemingly obvious relief that she was moving out.

She'd left all the expensive presents behind at his house and kept only her clothing, car and the key to her uncle's cabin in the mountains which he'd given her, along with permission to use it as long as he didn't have plans for entertaining his cronies at a hunting party.

But it was too early in the season for hunting. So, in her haste to get away, she hadn't bothered to make her usual check with his secretary before fleeing Georgetown.

Kara peered out the car window. Now she could barely make out the cabin's outline through the downpour. There was no sign of the rain letting up. Maybe coming here was a mistake, after all. She shivered. It was always colder in the mountains. And

10

the dampness was penetrating. But driving back to D.C. now was out of the question.

I guess I'm going to have to get really wet before I get dry again, she thought. Resolutely she opened the door, sloshed through the puddles to the back of the car, and pulled out her overnight case and handbag, which she carried to the cabin porch. Then she made another trip through the downpour to retrieve the groceries she'd bought.

With everything transferred to the porch, she heaved a sigh of relief and tried to blink the drops of water out of her thick black lashes. Then she unlocked the door and stepped quickly into the familiar shelter of the cabin.

Kara transferred her sodden grocery bags to the counter separating the kitchen from the living area and glanced at the massive fieldstone fireplace. Thank goodness George Mason from the village had already laid a fire. What she needed was to get out of her soaking wet jeans and apricot lambswool sweater and dry off.

Crossing the room, she searched the mantel for the long wooden matches Uncle James kept there and quickly lit the paper underneath the bed of dry wood. In moments a warming blaze had sprung up, casting long shadows across the room's rich cherry paneling.

Kara lifted a plaid wool blanket from the back of a nearby leather easy chair and spread it in front of the hearth. Then she began rummaging in her overnight bag for a towel and brush. Moments later she was pulling her wet sweater over her head.

"That's better," she murmured as she kicked off her clogs, unzipped her jeans and wriggled clear of the damp, clinging fabric. Clad only in silken bikini underpants and a matching beige lace bra that accented her slender but shapely curves, she toweled herself dry and then began to brush her raven curls by the inviting heat of the blazing logs.

Firelight gleamed warmly on her porcelain skin. And she felt the glow from the burning logs melt away the chilling effect from her wet clothes.

Relaxed and comfortable at last, she glanced around the spacious living room of the cabin. The flickering shadows gave the rustic furniture a mellow look. A sturdy, dark green leather sofa faced the fireplace, flanked by a matching leather and wood easy chair to its right. A colorful handmade quilt in the wedding ring pattern, folded over the arm of the sofa, added a bright touch of warmth.

A brass kerosene lamp occupied the end table. The cabin did have electricity, but Kara knew that the lamp stood ready for use in a power failure—a not uncommon occurrence in this remote mountain hideaway.

Rain was still pelting the cabin's roof, and Kara wondered idly if the storm might interrupt the power tonight. But it wouldn't really matter, she told herself. She wouldn't be watching the Friday night movie anyway, since the cabin's location precluded even marginal TV reception. And tonight she wasn't in the mood to listen to the radio or the tapedeck.

Kara stretched out on the plaid blanket, letting the warmth of the fire lull her into a peaceful lassitude. She could even let her mind wander to the subject of Wayne now without feeling so upset. When he had learned about the cabin, he had wanted to come up here with her, she remembered. But she'd been afraid of what would happen if they were alone together in such an isolated setting.

Should I have let him? she asked herself. But she knew instinctively that the answer was no. Don't worry about Wayne anymore, she told herself. It was so wonderfully comforting and drowsy by the fire. She would take a little nap and then fix some dinner.

She had just drifted off, her dark hair spread in a thick curtain over her shoulders, when she felt a gust of wind as the door suddenly flew open.

Jarred from the peaceful security she had just felt, Kara whipped her head around and her violet eyes opened wide. There framed in the doorway stood a dark, forceful stranger.

A look of surprise and then anger, mixed with something Kara couldn't quite fathom, crossed the man's features as he slammed the door and closed the distance between them in a few long strides.

Terrified, Kara clutched at her towel and tried to cover herself. But the stranger was undeterred. Grabbing her wrist in an iron grip, he pulled her ruthlessly to her feet. The towel slipped from her fingers.

"What the devil are you doing here?" he demanded. Grasping her shoulder, he administered a forceful shake that sent an electric shock down her spine.

"I hope for your sake you have a rational explanation for being half-naked in *my* cabin," he rasped menacingly, his eyes raking her body. "If this is another of Bill Thorp's attempts to discredit me, you'll both regret the day you agreed to this scheme!"

It took Kara a moment to recover from that initial shock and to find her voice. *"Your* cabin?" she finally managed to blurt out with more authority than she felt. "This happens to be my uncle's cabin and I have permission to use it. Just what gives you the right to walk in here without so much as knocking and threaten me?" she cried, lashing out at him with a clenched fist. But he merely laughed at her attempt to defend herself.

"Cut that out," he warned.

Sputtering with anger, Kara lowered her trembling arms. Ignoring her outrage, the stranger reached down, scooped up the fallen towel and thrust it at her.

"Cover yourself up," he said harshly. "I don't have time for one of Thorp's girls, though I have to admit he's showing better taste than I would have thought possible," he said, sweeping his eyes appraisingly over her scantily clad form.

Kara glared back as she pulled the towel around her body. Try to memorize what he looks like, she told herself, so you can give the police a good description.

Despite her fear, she forced herself to study him intently. Although she'd never met him before, he seemed vaguely familiar, as if she had seen his face once on television or in the papers. Maybe he was on the FBI's most-wanted list.

She had to admit he was handsome in a hard, ruthless sort of way. His thick, black hair, prematurely gray at the temples, glistened with droplets of water. The flinty gray eyes, set wide apart, and the strongly chiseled nose and chin gave him a compelling, arrogant appearance. He was tall, over six feet, with an athlete's powerful body of broad shoulders and narrow hips. The wet fabric of his wool slacks and flannel sport shirt clung to his muscular arms and hard thighs.

When he spoke, his voice was deep and vibrant, and still a bit menacing.

"I'm here for a meeting with James Barnett tomorrow. Since I had important business in Frederick this evening, he invited me to spend the night here so we could get right to work in the morning."

"Well that's too bad," Kara shot back. "You can't spend the night here. You'll just have to find other accommodations."

"We both know there are no other accommodations around here," he answered harshly, turning to retrieve his carryall from the porch.

As soon as his back was turned, Kara grabbed her jeans and sweater, now dry from the fire's heat. She had zipped up her pants and was struggling to find the armholes in her V-neck when she heard the stranger's sardonic laugh.

"Now that does make an interesting picture— being treated to a striptease in reverse. Maybe Bill Thorp's done me a favor after all."

His words set her raw nerves on edge. Yanking the sweater over her head, she shook her curly tresses free. Narrowing her normally wide eyes, she hissed, "Listen, mister, I don't know your Bill Thorp and I don't know why you're here, but you'd better get out of my uncle's cabin before I call the police."

"Nice try," he drawled with insolent amusement. "But I happen to know this cabin doesn't have a phone."

He was right she realized with horror. Uncle

James always boasted of the fact that this was his impenetrable retreat where no one could get hold of him except by having a message relayed through George Mason in the village.

"All right. Then *you* stay! But I'm getting out of here," she exclaimed, snatching up her purse and bag and heading for the door.

"Leaving without your shoes?" the maddening intruder called out just before she slammed the door.

It was still raining hard, and the soft mud was cold and slippery under her bare feet.

"I'd rather die than go back there," she muttered fiercely. She stumbled across the clearing and crawled into her car.

As the engine sprung to life, the door to the cabin was flung open and the man's tall figure emerged, striding purposefully toward the car and shouting something about the roads. Panic stricken, Kara slammed into reverse and tried to back out of the clearing and onto the dirt road. But her wheels spun uselessly.

As the stranger reached for the handle of the car door, she gunned the engine, sending a spray of muck onto his expensive-looking slacks and shirt. She heard him curse. An instant later he had yanked the door open and snatched the keys from the ignition.

"Just what do you think you're doing, you little idiot?" Roughly his strong hands grasped her, and she felt herself pulled from behind the wheel.

"Get your hands off me," she protested, trying to fight back. But in his grip, her struggles were as ineffectual as a child's. She felt herself hoisted in the air, slung over his shoulder, and then he was striding grimly back to the cabin.

"You beast, you animal!" she cried, pounding in helpless fury on his broad back. But he ignored the blows.

In a moment they were back in the cabin. With one hand he switched on the radio. Then he lowered Kara to the couch, holding her beside him in a vise-like clamp.

The strains of a popular song issued from the radio.

"What is that? Music to molest by?" Kara jeered, looking at him fiercely. But her anger turned to fear at the suddenly intense expression on his face.

"Not a bad idea," he murmured. Taking hold of the back of her neck, he drew her face slowly closer to his. His gray eyes locked with hers. She wanted to scream but the sound died in her throat as his warm mouth covered hers.

Her body stiffened in anger, but the hard pressure of his lips aroused a reaction she had not expected—a strange heat spread through her like a runaway flame as his lips explored hers. She'd never felt like this when Wayne kissed her.

She became so absorbed in this new sensation that she didn't notice the change in the radio broadcast—but he did. Abruptly he put her aside and reached over to turn up the volume.

Kara felt as though a pitcher of ice water had been dashed against her feverish skin and she realized with horror that she'd actually been enjoying his kiss.

"What do you think you're doing . . ." she started to gasp. But her captor pressed a tanned, muscular hand over her mouth.

"Quiet," he grated. "This is what I want you to hear."

". . . flash flooding in Frederick and Garrett counties. . . . Traveler's advisory warning. Highway 15 is under four feet of water and impassable. Flood waters are expected to recede by early morning."

"We're just going to have to put up with each other's company, for now," he said, smiling sardonically. "Neither one of us can leave this cabin. We're stuck with each other for the night."

Chapter Two

Wrenching herself free from his grasp, Kara leaped to her feet.

"Well, we may have to spend the night together, but you better believe it will be in separate rooms," she stormed.

"My, you are the proper young miss. Don't you think your Victorian theatrics have gone far enough?" he paused, considering. "You say you've never heard of Bill Thorp and you claim to have permission to use this cabin—so you must be one of Barnett's girlfriends. I've heard he likes his women young. But honestly, isn't he old enough to be your father?"

"He's older than my father by five years," the young woman snapped. "Haven't you been listening to a word I've said? James Barnett is my uncle. And

I'm Kara Barnett. Now I think you'd better tell me just exactly who you are," she challenged, putting her hands on her hips.

"For the politician's niece you claim to be, you don't seem to keep up with public affairs, do you? I'm Matthew Jordan—you know, the brash young politician who's challenging the crumbling old-line machine for control of the party in Maryland."

Kara's hand flew to her mouth to hide a gasp of surprise. Suddenly everything fell into place. She had seen his picture almost every day in the newspapers and on TV, but the media hadn't done justice to his rugged good looks and imposing virility.

Presently a state senator with an enviable record in Annapolis, he had recently announced his bid for Bill Thorp's U.S. congressional seat in the 6th District. And his campaign had promised personal accountability to voters.

But a cloud of suspicion crossed Kara's mind. What was this knight-errant of Maryland politics doing meeting with Uncle James, who represented the state's old-line politicians? Matt Jordan must be another wheeler-dealer after all—making promises he had no intention of keeping. And the way he was trifling with her tonight made that easy to believe.

"So you're just one of Uncle James' puppets," she accused.

"Your uncle and I are holding a press conference here tomorrow. You can read about our business in the afternoon newspapers. Until then, the subject is closed," he shot back, his eyes flat and hard.

Kara was searching her mind for an appropriate retort when her eyes widened in surprise. Matt

Jordan had slowly begun to unbutton his plaid flannel shirt, revealing a well-muscled chest covered with crisp, dark hairs.

Kara knew she should look away, but she found herself unable to drag her eyes from his well-proportioned body. An image of how it had felt to be caught in those arms and held against that unyielding chest flashed through her mind. Angrily she dismissed the disturbing picture.

His muscles rippled as he tossed the shirt carelessly onto the sofa and reached to undo the monogrammed brass buckle on his leather belt.

"Surely you're not going to take off your clothes in front of me?" she gasped.

"Why not—turnabout's fair play," he taunted. "Besides, I'm soaking wet and covered with mud from your temper tantrum out in the car. I want to change into something dry. And I suggest you do the same. You look first cousin to a drowned cat."

Kara flushed to the roots of her dark hair. Matt Jordan was unzipping his pants and in a moment they would be off, too.

Grabbing her overnight case, she fled through the bedroom and into its adjoining bathroom, locking the door firmly behind her. She pressed her fingertips to her temples, trying to calm her jumbled thoughts. So many emotions were racing through her brain that she was unable to sort them out.

Matt Jordan had upset her in a way no other man had done before—not even Wayne with his constant pressure to share his bed. What's wrong with me? she asked herself in disgust. I mustn't lose control like this. I'm behaving like an adolescent schoolgirl.

I'll bet if I had just stood my ground I could have called his bluff. But deep down she knew it hadn't been a bluff.

Firmly erasing Matt Jordan's mocking image from her mind's eye, she focused her attention on her own face in the mirror. I do look a mess, she thought, pushing back a dark curl from her forehead. Her delicate face was flushed and framed in a riot of unkempt raven ringlets. There was a smudge of mud on her right cheek. And her eyes seemed almost twice their normal size.

Maybe I'll feel more able to cope with the situation after a shower, she thought. Kara reached down and began to tug her mud-spotted apricot sweater over her head. But the movement reminded her of the way Matt Jordan's eyes had lingered upon her earlier in the evening. Hastily, she reached over and checked the lock on the bathroom door. It was tightly secured. Reassured, she took off her clothes, turned the water on full, and stepped into the shower stall.

The warm needle spray felt invigorating and buoyed up her spirits. I can deal with Matt Jordan, she thought. He probably makes a pass at every halfway attractive woman he meets. And they're all thrilled to receive the attentions of an up and coming man of power. But it's not going to work with me, she assured herself firmly.

Ten minutes later she stepped purposefully from the stall. Briskly she toweled herself with a large red bath sheet she found in the linen closet and dried her hair with a blow dryer, combing and arranging her curls. Then she rummaged in her bag for clean, dry clothes. She chose a pair of navy blue corduroys and a lavender Western shirt that matched her eyes and emphasized their unusual color.

After dressing, she applied a dab of gloss to her pale lips. Now that's better, she thought, giving the image she saw an approving nod. But the next moment her satisfaction turned to disgust and she wiped off the gloss with a tissue. She didn't want that arrogant Matt Jordan to think she was doing anything special to attract him.

Kara threw open the bathroom door and stepped onto the thick yellow shag carpet of the bedroom. Crossing the room, she set her bag beside the king-size quilt-covered bed. Next she pulled out her leather moccasin slippers and sat down on the bed to put them on. But the mattress swayed under her and she leapt to her feet. Why that uncle of mine has put a water bed in here, she thought, giving the mattress a push with her palm to confirm her suspicions. The gossip I've been hearing since I left must be true. And I thought Uncle James just used this place for hunting parties. No wonder that crony of his out there got the wrong idea about me.

Kara was about to sit down in the wooden rocker near the rain-streaked window, when the tantalizing smell of bacon and eggs wafted through the bedroom door. She'd only had a bite to eat at lunch. And now it was nine o'clock, she thought, glancing at her watch. She was starving!

Quickly pulling on her slippers and switching off the bedroom light, Kara opened the door into the cabin's main room. From where she stood in the shadows, she could observe the brightly lit kitchen without being seen.

Matt Jordan, dressed casually in jeans and a gray

23

pullover open at the neck, was standing at the counter-top stove, expertly stirring a skillet of fluffy yellow eggs. A plate of crisp bacon strips was nearby.

Kara watched him in silence. She had to admit there was something magnetic about his rugged good looks. His features were strongly defined. His neck was a proud bronze column above the open V of his pullover. His body, though muscular, moved with an effortless grace. Despite herself, Kara felt her emotions responding to the attraction of his masculinity. But one portion of her mind remained cool.

Don't get carried away, she told herself fiercely. You hardly know that man—and what you do know about him is all bad. He's a conceited, opportunistic politician who's into some dirty dealings with Uncle James. Pressing her lips into a tight line, she walked further into the room.

Matt Jordan looked up and favored her with a friendly smile. But she wasn't about to respond in kind.

"Isn't this marvelous," she said caustically. "I can see you're a man of many talents. You can fry bacon and scramble eggs as well as manhandle women."

"Being a bachelor has sharpened my skills in many areas," he replied, grinning rakishly now.

"I'll just bet," she returned, angry that a blush was once again spreading across her cheeks.

She reached to pull out one of the antique pressed-oak chairs at the kitchen table. But a firm hand on her shoulder restrained her. She could feel Matt Jordan's warm breath on her neck.

"Not so fast," he said. "I'm not going to do all the work while you sit at the table like a lady of leisure. Fix the toast and start the coffee. And then get the table set."

Though Kara seethed at his high-handed manner, she realized that his request was a fair one. Biting her lower lip to keep from making a retort, she set about following his directions.

The kitchen was planned for one-person efficiency. A row of honey-brown wood cabinets across the wall held all the necessary dishes and silverware. Kara was acutely aware of Matthew Jordan's presence as she brushed past him standing at the stove. His peremptory manner grated, and she couldn't help slamming the plates onto the table and clattering the coffee cups before she filled them.

"Take it easy," he admonished. "You don't want your uncle to find all the crockery broken, do you?"

"He can afford it. And anyway, I don't care what Uncle James finds."

"Aren't you fond of your uncle?" he inquired, coolly fixing her with an appraising glance.

"He may be my only relative, but he's always had more time for politics than his orphaned niece," she retorted. Yet inwardly she knew her show of temper was really directed at the man who sat across from her, not her Uncle James.

Matt Jordan stared at her quizzically, but she ignored the questioning look in his eyes as she began to eat the bacon and eggs he had just dished out. The first forkful made Kara realize just how hungry she really was. She concentrated on her food, ignoring the disturbing man who was sharing the simple meal with her. But once the last mouthful had disappeared from her plate, she looked up to find Matt's eyes fixed on her in a penetrating gaze.

"I guess my cooking can't be that bad after all," he observed.

"Almost anyone can scramble eggs," she parried. "But maybe your publicity writer can turn it into something spectacular. From that ad campaign you've had on TV, anyone would think you're Superman in disguise. You come across too good to be true."

Matt raised an eyebrow at her criticism. "Maybe you'd better explain yourself a little better," he challenged.

"What I mean is your campaign isn't showing any human side of you. You need to step down from that pedestal your ads have put you on and show that you can relate to real people—like a real human being."

"And just what qualifies you to tell me how to run my campaign? Where do you get this wealth of critical analysis?" he shot back.

"I'm a public relations specialist with Citizens for Consumer Protection," she replied smugly. "I know what goes over with the public."

"And how long have you been with them? Six months?"

Kara felt her face grow hot. How had he guessed? But Matt Jordan gave her no time to mount a defense.

"I'm always interested in a fresh approach," he said smoothly. "What would you do if you were running my campaign?"

"I'd try to portray you as less of a tin god. I'd show you as a human being who can relate to other

26

people." Kara's eyes widened with excitement as the thought of how it would be to manage a major political campaign flashed through her mind.

"That's an intriguing idea," he drawled as he pushed his chair back from the table and stood up. "Why don't we try out some of your ideas right now," he suggested, walking around the table and draping his arms over Kara's shoulder. "You don't know how unbending I can really be," he added huskily.

Kara's mind was a jumble of confusion. Would this important politician really listen to her opinion? she wondered. But she had little time to think. Matt Jordan had drawn her chair firmly away from the table. In a swift motion he caught her under her elbows and pulled her smoothly to her feet.

"I think the couch is a more appropriate place to put some of your theories into practice." Everything happened so quickly that Kara was thoroughly confused. Dazedly she let herself be led across the living room. But when he pulled her down on the couch she suddenly realized his real intentions.

"You aren't really interested in my PR expertise at all," she accused, trying to free herself from the steel band of his arms. But he ignored her protest.

"Kara, can't you feel the chemistry between us?" he murmured, his lips against her hair.

She tried to deny it. But the warmth of his breath on her neck and the male scent of his body so close to hers had a devastating effect on her senses. Brushing her hair back, he caressed the sensitive spot behind her ears as his lips trailed feather light kisses down her neck.

Quicksilver flame coursed through Kara's veins.

Of their own volition her arms slid around his neck. Suddenly, unaccountably she wanted to fit the soft curves of her body closer to the unyielding hardness of his.

Sensations she had never dreamed of kindled in the very center of her being. It was as though Matt Jordan had control of her body. Every kiss, every touch, struck a responsive chord that she had no power to fight.

His lips teased the sensitive hollow at the base of her throat. His strong hands moved down her shoulders to the curve of her back. Then he caught her under her knees and she felt her feet being pulled off the floor, her legs being stretched out on the couch.

"Don't deny you want this too," he whispered huskily in her ear. "I can feel the way your body is trembling."

A warning light flashed in Kara's brain. Here she was being seduced by a man she'd known less than three hours. She forced herself to a sitting position on the couch and said in a not too steady voice, "I think this political discussion has gotten out of hand, Mr. Jordan."

"If you'd give in to your real feelings, we could plot my campaign strategy well into the night," he said, trying to draw her back into his warm embrace.

But she dodged aside and sprang to her feet. She didn't look back till she had reached her bedroom door.

Matt's gray eyes were flinty hard. "Your reputation as a tease is still intact, Miss Barnett. But let me assure you the primaries aren't over yet," he threatened.

Not wanting to hear another word, Kara slammed the door and turned the key with a loud click. That man has made a fool of me twice, she thought. Oh how I hate him, she added, crossing over to the bed and pulling the covers back with a savage yank. She began to fluff up the pillows, giving them hard jabs as she thought about the way he was probably laughing at her right now. She paced around the room, but it was hard to calm her emotions.

Still angry, Kara fumbled in her overnight bag for her nightgown. Pulling it out, she realized that she'd forgotten how cold it was in the mountains. The light blue, sleeveless nylon gown she'd packed would offer little protection against the cold.

Shivering, she looked out the window. Rain was coming down in sheets again, and now she could hear the low rumble of thunder in the distance. How she wished she could open the door to let some of the warmth of the fireplace into the bedroom. But that was impossible with Matt Jordan in the cabin.

Kara switched on the waterbed heater and crossed to the bathroom. She brushed her teeth and washed her face before quickly changing into her gown. Glancing at herself in the mirror, she realized her nightdress was more revealing than she remembered. But it wouldn't matter since she wasn't planning to see Matt Jordan until she was fully dressed in the morning.

Crawling into the waterbed, she pulled the covers up to her chin. The bed swayed beneath her weight and the sheets were still cold. The unaccustomed motion made it hard to get comfortable. For warmth, she drew up her knees and tucked her head under the covers, leaving the barest air hole for breathing. How am I ever going to get to sleep? she thought, feeling the waterbed move under her body. Outside, in the main room, she could hear Matt Jordan poking up the fire. Was the lock on her bedroom door strong enough to keep him out? she wondered. But she knew it should be, since Uncle James always made sure everything in his cabin was the best.

It was hard for Kara to settle down, but the events of the day had left their toll on her body as well as her mind. Finally she drifted off into a restless, troubled sleep.

Suddenly she was jolted from an uneasy dream by an awful crash above her head. Sitting bolt upright, she heard herself scream. Had the deafening noise been part of a nightmare? It wasn't a dream— something was happening. The house shook as another crash sounded in her ear and she looked about wildly, finally looking up. Plaster was falling from above where the huge limb of a tree protruded through the ceiling. The heavy branch shook, spattering icy water about the room.

Kara threw the covers aside and rushed from her bed. She fumbled for the light switch and flipped it. But nothing happened. At the same time, she heard Matt Jordan's concerned voice through the closed door.

"Kara, what's happened? Are you all right?" he questioned urgently. She could hear him rattling the lock.

"I—I don't know," she stammered, feeling dazed and disoriented. Just then the tree above her gave a groan and shifted further into the ceiling. A branch raked through her thick black hair, holding her prisoner. She screamed again, beside herself with hysterical terror. The more she struggled, the tighter the prickly branches clutched her.

"Unlock the door," Matt Jordan ordered. But she was unable to obey.

"All right, then stand clear. I'm coming in." She heard the lock give under the thrust of his powerful shoulder. In a moment he was beside her. Taking in the situation in one, comprehensive glance, he disengaged her tangled hair and folded her into the protection of his strong arms. She felt the soft flannel of his robe against her cheek.

"This tree could fall at any minute," he rasped. "Let's get out of here. Lifting her effortlessly in his arms, he carried her into the living room where he sat down and cradled her gently on the blanket still spread in front of the fire.

Kara clung to his strong body like a frightened child, shaking as another bolt of lightning hit close to the house.

"It was horrible," she sobbed.

"It's all right; you're safe now," he soothed, gently stroking her hair as he rocked her back and forth in his arms. His strong hands were amazingly gentle as they massaged the back of her neck and her shoulders, easing the tension from her body. Gradually she relaxed in his arms.

"Please, don't leave me alone," she murmured as she snuggled closer to his protective presence. For an answer he drew the circle of his arms tighter.

Her last thought before she drifted into a peaceful sleep was that his embrace was like a calm harbor in the storm. She was unaware when he gently lowered her to the blanket, lay down beside her, and covered them both with the quilt he had pulled from the arm of the couch.

Chapter Three

Kara awoke with a start. She was suddenly aware of several very disturbing sensations. Her shoulders were cold, for the blanket had slipped away in the night leaving her upper body covered only by the silky nightgown. A muscular arm was wrapped around her waist and her hip was pinned beneath a hard, unyielding male thigh. And she could hear sounds of car doors slamming outside and crunching footsteps approaching the house.

"The roads were so muddy I wasn't sure we were going to make it," a disgruntled voice said.

"Oh, come on, you'd go barefoot through a monsoon to get an interview like this," an answering voice jibed. "Just be glad this place is on high ground and Jordan didn't have to swim for it last night."

"Good heavens, look at that tree," a female exclaimed. "It's gone right through the roof. I wonder if Jordan's all right."

In the next instant the cabin door was flung open and several people crowded into the room. The chattering of the intruders stopped abruptly as they took in the still entwined twosome on the floor in front of the huge stone fireplace. Kara stared in horror as realization dawned.

"Oh no!" She shuddered, noting the shocked expressions in the seven pairs of eyes looking down at her. It was obvious what they were thinking. Expressions of astonishment, anger, chagrin and sly amusement crossed their faces as they gazed at her almost naked body pinned beneath Matt Jordan's powerful sleeping form.

"Well now, doesn't that make a pretty picture," one man commented wryly, grinning and lifting the camera hung around his neck to his face. A flash bulb popped, and in the next instant Matt Jordan sat up.

"What the hell is going on?" he exclaimed, brushing back a lock of dark hair that had slipped over his forehead and glaring at the crowd of reporters and cameramen confronting them.

"Shouldn't we be the ones asking that question?" snapped a female voice. Kara looked up at the tall redheaded woman in the finely tailored wool suit who had made the remark. The redhead's hard green eyes swerved to Uncle James' still astonished face.

"I see you provide your politicians with fringe benefits," she observed cattily. A dull red flush crept over the older man's wrinkled visage. His heavy eyebrows snapped together in anger as he took in her meaning.

"Wait until they see this one on the six o'clock news," she added. "Matt Jordan won't look like a knight in shining armor when the voters see what his extracurricular activities consist of.''

A TV cameraman had already aimed his minicam at the startled couple in front of the fireplace. But Uncle James interposed his short, rotund form between them.

"Just a minute here," he said, wiping beads of perspiration from his brow. "You can be sued for invasion of privacy if you publish . . ." he sought for words, "if you photograph an intimate scene of a honeymoon couple without their permission. Jordan and my niece obviously didn't realize that we'd be coming so early—the roads were under water last night you know," he said, thinking quickly.

Kara's jaw dropped open. She gasped and crossed her bare arms protectively in front of her breasts. Expressions of surprise from the intruders mixed with nervous laughter greeted her ears. She blushed.

"Oh no," exclaimed Kara, "we were . . . I mean I was," she stammered. But her explanation was quickly stifled by Matt Jordan who had seized her upper arm, wrapping his hard fingers around it tightly. She flinched.

"Be quiet. You got us into this. Don't make it any worse," he murmured through clenched teeth. "My career is at stake."

Futilely she tried to jerk her arm free from his iron grasp. Looking to her uncle for help, she met only his frowning stare. His stern expression told her to be silent. Dimly Kara was aware of a blonde young woman directly behind her uncle. The woman stepped forward to touch James' arm in a fruitless attempt to calm him. But the irate politician shook her off.

She must be one of his new girlfriends, Kara thought fleetingly. But her uncle's meaningful gaze brought her quickly back to the situation at hand.

Adroitly the aging politician announced to the curious onlookers, "We hadn't planned to make this public until the end of the press conference, but now is as good a time as any—my niece Kara Barnett and Matt Jordan were married in a private ceremony yesterday. They came here to honeymoon before Mr. Jordan's press conference."

Excited chatter and nervous laughter filled the room.

"You can sure keep a secret, Frank," Kara heard a reporter needle a tall, thin man with colorless hair.

"Well, even a campaign manager doesn't have to tell everything," he responded weakly.

"How long have they been engaged?" the reporter persisted. But before the campaign manager could answer, a loud voice in the crowd asserted itself.

"What county did you get married in?" the red-headed television reporter inquired sharply of Matt Jordan. "I'm sure our viewers will be fascinated and would love to know all the details." She emphasized the word "love," but the expression on her face was anything but warm. "Matt—aren't you the sly one—running off with this little girl," she shot Kara a look of amused condescension. "You're full of surprises —but then so am I."

The reporter turned to face Kara, her brilliant crimson lipstick outlining a tight smile. "I've been working very closely with Matt, and I'm interested in making sure he gets good press," she purred. "So naturally I'm fascinated by this *terribly* romantic development." Her appraising green eyes raked over Kara's flimsy blue nightdress. "I'm Vera Caldwell," she continued. "I'm sure you've seen me on the Channel 12 news. I specialize in political stories."

Kara felt ridiculous—like some foolish secretary caught on the boss' lap with her blouse undone. But she hadn't spent years in a girls' boarding school where verbal duels were a daily occurrence without learning a tactic or two to defend herself. Mustering her strength, she looked back at the smartly dressed television reporter.

"No, I don't think so, but then I only have time to watch the more important local stations," Kara shot back. An unattractive flush of anger crossed the reporter's carefully made up face, but before she had an opportunity to retaliate, Kara, determined to keep her dignity, stood up and walked resolutely to the half-open bedroom door. But she was forced to stop abruptly when she remembered the tree. Quickly she recrossed the room, acutely conscious of everyone's eyes upon her partially clad body and disappeared into the guest bedroom. As soon as she had closed the door behind her, she collapsed on the bed, confused, angry and tearful.

She was just trying to pull herself together a few minutes later when Matt Jordan, toting his carryall and her overnight bag, joined her.

"How could you?" she flared at him angrily,

looking up from where she still huddled on the bed. "How could you agree that we were married?"

"What the hell else could I do?" he retorted, setting down the luggage and grasping her bare shoulders in his strong, warm hands. "Now listen to me. You got me into this and you're going to get me out. We'll have to get married."

"Married!" Kara shrieked, almost beside herself. "Are you crazy?" Instantly Jordan clapped his forceful hand over her mouth and held it there despite Kara's struggles to free herself.

"Quiet," he hissed. "Do you want them to hear you out there? Now listen to me. You'll do as I say. We're going to be married. As soon as possible—this afternoon, if it can be managed."

Tearing herself away from him, she fled to the other side of the room, putting the distance of the bed between them. Her hands clutched the edge of the large mahogany bureau for support.

"This is intolerable," she moaned. "What am I going to do?" But even as she uttered those words, a series of images flashed seductively through her mind. She saw her friends and co-workers looking astonished and envious as they heard the announcement of her marriage to the handsome congressional candidate—and Wayne's chagrin and mortification upon hearing the news. She saw the redheaded reporter's green-eyed jealousy as Matt Jordan smiled down at his new raven-haired bride. And finally, she saw her soft, yielding body swept up in Matt Jordan's powerful embrace. With a shiver she admitted to herself that this final image was the most appealing of all.

But quickly she dismissed the last picture from her mind. She simply could not allow herself to be attracted to this overbearing political opportunist. Marriage was too important to Kara. She knew that when she married it would be for love. Matt Jordan was a stranger who didn't love or even care about her. She sighed. I couldn't live with that kind of relationship, she told herself. She had felt alone and unloved for too long. No, marriage was too important to be taken so lightly.

Suddenly she became aware of Matt Jordan's assessing gaze. She looked up and blushed. His eyes were wandering speculatively over her scantily clad form.

"Maybe marriage between us wouldn't be so bad, at least for a while," he mused aloud. His suggestive gaze lingered on her breasts, barely concealed beneath the thin material of her nightdress.

Lifting his eyes to hers, he stalked across the room. To Kara he looked like some predatory beast after his helpless prey. Confused by the purpose she read in his eyes, she stepped back only to find herself trapped in the corner between the bed and the massive mahogany dresser.

She raised her hands futilely to ward off his determined advances, but he merely seized her wrists in a strong viselike grip and smiling, lifted her hands above her head, pinning her helplessly between his overwhelming maleness and the wall. His cool gray eyes slid speculatively over her fine features, finally resting on her soft, half-parted lips. Slowly he bent his dark head, and his mouth moved to take possession of hers. Snapping to, Kara quickly

39

closed her mouth in a hard line of defense, but undeterred, Matt continued to probe her lips, his kiss insistently demanding.

Helplessly she tried to twist her body from his relentless assault. But her efforts only seemed to heighten his desire. He pressed his hard thighs and hips against her vulnerable form.

Against her will, she felt her mouth betray her and her moist lips parted, welcoming his probing tongue. A warm surge of desire flickered through her, and she felt her hips mold themselves to his in response.

Lifting his head, Matt Jordan smiled tauntingly into her deep, violet eyes. "See what I mean," he drawled. "You know, I wouldn't be surprised if you had something like this in mind last night when you begged me not to leave you. It wouldn't be the first time that an enterprising young miss trapped an eligible bachelor into marriage."

His words enveloped her like cold wind, sweeping away her earlier fevered passion. Wide-eyed, she stared incredulously at him. He was actually suggesting that she had deliberately trapped him into this unwanted contract. The conceit of such an assumption made her furious. Her pale skin went white with rage and her eyes gleamed with anger. If he's arrogant enough to think I would trick him into a loveless marriage, she thought perversely, then maybe that's just the kind of marriage he deserves.

"Yes," she replied between gritted teeth, "I will marry you!"

"I thought so," he commented wryly, his eyes glittering dangerously. He pulled away from her and gave her body a last marauding glance.

But suddenly his gaze was broken by the sound of an urgent rapping at the door. "You better get out here," boomed the voice of his campaign manager, Frank Adams. "These reporters are getting restless."

Cursing softly, Matt Jordan turned from his still seething prospective bride. Moments later he had dressed and left the room while Kara watched in silent fury.

It wasn't long before her anger subsided though, and she began to have second thoughts about her impetuous decision. Outside the door the press conference had started, and she could hear the voices of Matt, Uncle James, Adams and the questioning reporters. Her hands flew to her head as her mind began to clear.

"Oh, what am I doing?" she almost wailed aloud. Quickly she pulled her white overnight bag off the plaid lounge chair and began feverishly emptying it. In a minute she had found fresh underwear, her hairbrush, clean blue jeans and a burgundy pullover. Anxiously she fumbled with the zipper on her jeans and had trouble maneuvering her arms through the sweater. Dressed at last, she opened the door, firmly intent on interrupting the press conference and setting the record straight.

But she had gone only a few paces when Uncle James swooped down on her and herded her into the kitchen. Over her shoulder she could see Matt Jordan showing the crowd of reporters out. As they exited, Frank Adams paused and whispered with him urgently. Matt shrugged and shook his head. Both men turned and cast quick glances at Kara—

the campaign manager's hostile, the candidate's unreadable. Then Adams left to continue conciliating the reporters.

The moment the front door closed Uncle James turned to Kara and demanded, "What the hell were you doing here? You've really made a fine mess of things, young lady!"

"Ah . . . um . . ." Kara started to stammer, trying to formulate an answer, but her uncle's angry stare made her unable to continue. Again Kara noticed the blonde in the background who was shooting her condemning looks. She watched curiously as the woman turned solicitously to Uncle James.

"Here, drink this," the woman insisted, thrusting a pill and a glass into the agitated man's hands.

"I don't need that now, Monica," he said, firmly dismissing her offer and turning back to his niece. "The only solution to this mess is to get you two married—and quickly." He knit his brow, obviously deep in thought. Then his expression cleared. "Lucky for us, Maryland doesn't require a waiting period between getting a license and having the ceremony. We can have the whole thing arranged and taken care of before those reporters get back to Baltimore and Washington to make liars of us." Then casting a concerned look at Kara, James added, "You can divorce after the election if you want, but until then you'd better be the most convincing pair of lovebirds in political history."

"But I don't love him. I hardly know him!" Kara cried. "This whole thing is a huge misunderstanding!" She wheeled around and pointed an accusing finger at Matt, whose lithe, muscular body was lounging indolently in the doorway.

"She's right," he drawled, "but that doesn't change things. We'll still have to get married."

"But I can't; I won't. . . ." Kara sputtered.

"You can and you must," her uncle stated firmly. He gave her a level look. "Kara, start thinking straight. This doesn't just affect Jordan. It will have disastrous effects on your reputation as well. You have a budding career in public relations in Washington. But a scandal could wreck it before it got off the ground."

Kara's eyes fell. Although her thoughts were in turmoil, she knew that her uncle's words had validity. She had only been working in the capital a few months, but she knew what the scandal sheets would do with a story like this.

"And then there's Jordan's career," her uncle went on. "This congressional election could be just a stepping-stone to higher office—possibly the presidency—and a scandal could ruin everything."

Kara looked over at Matt Jordan's dark, handsome figure in the doorway. Was it really true that he might someday be president? Did she really hold the political future of the country in her hand? Would it be selfish and ridiculous to stand in his way? Torn between her warring emotions, she sank down weakly in the kitchen chair and put her head in her hands.

"All right, go ahead and arrange the wedding," she capitulated in a barely audible voice.

The next few hours were a blur of confused sensations. Once she had given in to Uncle James' arguments, the older man had immediately sprung to action, issuing staccato orders at his female companion and his driver. He made arrangements for a pre-dated marriage license and for a local justice of the peace from the village to come up and marry the reluctant couple.

When Kara realized that her uncle meant to hold the ceremony almost immediately, she protested, "But I can't get married in blue jeans. You're making a mockery of this whole thing. It's nothing more than a charade," she cried, throwing up her hands in despair.

But James brushed her objections aside. "Come on now, Kara," he chuckled, "your generation doesn't bother much with white satin nowadays. And if you wanted to march down the aisle in virgin white you should've thought twice about spending the night wrapped up with Jordan here," he teased. The fact that her uncle was getting his own way had put him in a good humor.

But his light tone did not make Kara feel any better. Up until yesterday she had been in command of her life, but now she was being swept up in a flood of events over which she had no control. She blinked away the tears that were stinging the backs of her eyes.

Unexpectedly, Matt Jordan, who had been watching the scene in silence, moved toward the small figure. Taking her cold hands in his, Matt searched her tear-filled eyes for a long moment and then said in a gentle voice, "Kara, I know this isn't what you wanted—it's not exactly what I had in mind either. But the circumstances have forced our hands. We have no choice. We have to be married as quickly as possible. You'll be a more beautiful bride in blue jeans than most women are in white satin." He leaned over and planted a soft kiss on her forehead. "And I promise you that after we're married your closet will be filled with silk and lace."

His unexpected kindness unleashed the tears Kara had fought so bravely to hold back. She sobbed helplessly against his shoulder. But Matt Jordan lifted her chin and looked down into her clouded eyes. "Okay?" he inquired softly. All Kara could do was nod and look away from his steady gaze.

He led her to the door of the bedroom. "You need to relax for a while. Why don't you lie down and rest until the justice of the peace arrives," he told her. She nodded again, went into the bedroom and closed the door.

Images flashed before her—Matt Jordan's handsome face and her uncle's look of agitation, the tree branch in the ceiling of her bedroom, the catlike eyes of the redheaded reporter. But she couldn't get them in focus. One merged into another and it was impossible to interpret any one of them accurately. As the pictures whirled through her mind, she grew dizzy and sat down heavily on the quilt-covered bed.

It seemed like only a few minutes before Matt was rapping firmly on the door and then leading her out into the main room of the cabin where everyone stood waiting.

They were married in front of the big stone fireplace. The justice of the peace, a small, bespectacled man with thinning sandy hair, cast curious, surreptitious glances at the blue-jeaned couple standing dazedly before him.

"Do you take this woman to be your lawfully wedded wife?" he read from a printed sheet of paper, frowning slightly and looking up questioningly at Matt. "To honor in sickness and in health as long as you both shall live?"

"I do," Matt replied in a steady voice.

The official then turned to the distracted Kara and repeated the question. There was a long pause while she stared wildly at the man's bewildered face. She had never felt so alone. She cast a desperate look at her bridegroom who nodded reassuringly back at her. From the other side of her Kara could feel her uncle silently willing her to say "yes." Even the slender blonde who hovered at Uncle James' side seemed to be allied against her. The tension was more than she could bear as all eyes focused on her.

"I do," she whispered in a dull voice. And then it was all over. There was an almost audible sigh of relief as the tension dissipated in the room.

"Repeat after me, 'With this ring I thee wed,'" the official hurried on. Kara hadn't thought about the ring. What, she wondered, would Matt Jordan use? But he seemed unconcerned as he turned toward her, drew a fine garnet ring from his pocket and slipped it over Kara's slender finger. It fit perfectly, and Kara felt an involuntary twinge of pleasure as she looked down at the jewel sparkling on her hand. How would he have found time to rush down into the village and purchase it? she wondered. She smiled up at him as he leaned over to kiss her warmly on the mouth. Her spirits lifted despite herself.

"By the power vested in me by the state of Maryland," continued the justice of the peace, "I declare you husband and wife." Kara and Matt Jordan embraced once again and Uncle James, wiping his brow in relief, pecked Kara on the cheek.

"That's a good girl," he whispered to the new bride. "We'll straighten this mess out later."

As Uncle James stepped back, the blonde moved forward and said, "Congratulations." She embraced Kara in a formal hug. The new bride received the woman's attentions stiffly.

"Thank you," she muttered in reply, trying to make her gratitude sound genuine. But it was difficult for her to conceal the feelings of disapproval she had toward the woman who must be Uncle James' latest playmate.

Out of the corner of her eye, Kara saw her uncle slip the justice a crisp $100 bill. Then the little man hurried out the door.

Turning to Matt, she looked shyly up at the tall, handsome figure at her side. "The ring is beautiful," she murmured. "However did you find the time to pick it out for me? And how did you know my ring size?" She looked up at him in surprised admiration.

"I didn't," he confessed casually. "And the ring size was just luck. The ring belongs to Monica, who was kind enough to lend it to us for the wedding. You'd better return it to her now. We'll get you something of your own later."

Kara felt herself going cold. Quickly she stripped the ring off her finger and thrust it into Monica's outstretched hand. "That was thoughtful of you," Kara said through gritted teeth.

"Oh, it was nothing," the cool blonde replied, slipping the gem back on her well-manicured finger.

To Kara the ring that she had momentarily treasured seemed now a symbol of this whole farce of a marriage. It was nothing but a sham. She stared bleakly at her bare ring finger and wondered what lay ahead.

Chapter Four

Kara sank down into the black leather bucket seat of Matt's silver gray Porsche. She half-listened to the low throb of the powerful engine as her new husband expertly swung out of the cabin's drive and headed the shiny sportscar toward Washington, D.C.

Behind them, Uncle James' black Lincoln Continental turned off in the opposite direction toward the village. He and his companion were speeding away to file the pre-dated marriage papers at the County Courthouse and speak to the caretaker about cutting up the fallen tree and repairing the damage to the roof.

As Kara and Matt flew past rolling green hills, weathered barns and silos, and pastures full of grazing cows, Matt began enumerating the tasks that had to be done before the day's end. But when he told her in an assured voice that they would first stop at her apartment to get some of her clothes before going to his town house in Columbia, Kara sat up straight and glared at him in outrage.

"Surely you don't think I'm going to move in with you?" she protested. "Why, I hardly know you. I thought this marriage was only going to be a show for your campaign. Nobody said we actually had to live together." She shot an angry look at his handsome profile.

Matt's mouth twisted in a grimace of sardonic amusement. "It will be a show all right," he conceded. "But if we start the opening act of our marriage by living in different cities, the press will treat it like a circus sideshow. You wouldn't want that would you?" he asked her with a derisive glint in his steely gray eyes.

"I don't care about the press. I'm not sleeping with you," she insisted, continuing to stare stubbornly at him.

"I've been told I'm a perfectly congenial bed-partner," he remarked as he swung the car smoothly around a sharp turn. "I don't snore, I don't hog the blankets. And I'm fun to snuggle with on a cold night," he teased. "But if you're determined to sleep alone, there are two guest bedrooms in my town house. You'd better lock your doors, though," he warned with a laugh, "because I've been known to sleepwalk."

Kara tried to suppress the grin tugging at the corners of her mouth, but it broke out despite her efforts. She had to admit he was right. It would look suspicious if they started the marriage living apart.

"All right," she grudgingly agreed. "But remember, I'm not sharing your bed!"

"Okay," he said without emotion. "The spare bedroom is yours."

Kara sighed. At least the ground rules were understood. Feeling less tense, she closed her eyes and leaned back against the deep upholstery. The day was not yet half over and already she was exhausted.

Forty-five minutes later she awoke with a start. The Porsche had come to an abrupt stop in front of the aging brick town house in Georgetown where she shared a tiny apartment with Jill Sanders. The familiarity of her surroundings made the day's events seem even more bizarre. How was she going to explain Matt Jordan to her inquisitive roommate? she wondered nervously.

As Kara climbed the narrow front steps while Matt locked the car door, she hurriedly tried to frame an explanation of the unannounced marriage. But before she could think of anything the varnished wood front door was flung open and Kara almost collided with a hastily exiting Jill.

"Oh Kara, I've been hoping you'd come back before I left," her roommate declared breathlessly. "You've gotten a couple of phone messages and oh, by the way, you'll be glad to hear that Wayne stopped by. He said to tell you yesterday was all a mistake. He wants to have dinner with you tonight— to talk," she added, giving Kara a meaningful wink. "He'll be . . ." Jill stopped midsentence as she noticed the tall, commanding presence of Matt Jordan who had climbed the steps and laid a heavy, possessive hand on Kara's slim shoulder.

"Oh," Jill gasped, putting her hand to her mouth. "I didn't realize . . ."

"Allow me to introduce myself. I'm Matt Jordan, Kara's husband," he announced. "Kara and I were married yesterday and she won't be keeping that appointment with the gentleman you mentioned." His voice dripped with sarcasm as he eyed Kara's astonished roommate coldly.

Jill's mouth dropped open while she searched vainly for a response. But all she could get out were flustered congratulations mixed with quizzical stares at her friend. Kara received Jill's confused congratulations woodenly. She didn't know what to say.

"Well, I have to be going. I was on my way to a meeting," her friend stammered. She stared blankly at Kara for a moment and then leaned forward to give her a kiss on the cheek. Kara seized this opportunity to whisper in Jill's ear.

"It's all right. I'll call you later and explain."

But even as she said the words, Kara found herself wondering how she could possibly explain any of this.

As soon as Jill disappeared down the brick-paved sidewalk, the newlyweds stepped inside Kara's tiny, neatly appointed apartment. Closing the door, Matt swept the living room with an appraising glance. Despite its small size it was elegantly and expensively furnished. On the floor a magnificent Chinese rug with gold and ivory design caught his eye. And around the room fine antiques upholstered in shades of blue and gold were set off by the polished sheen of mahogany Queen Anne tables and a Sheraton desk.

Quizzically, Matt raised a dark eyebrow. "This isn't a typical struggling young career girl's apartment. How do you afford such luxury?"

Kara stiffened and shot him an angry look. "The

furniture happens to have belonged to my parents," she countered.

Matt shrugged, his eyes resting thoughtfully on a blue velvet loveseat. "Well, they certainly had good taste," he conceded. "But there's hardly room to turn around here. Where do you entertain this Wayne when your roommate's at home?" he baited, giving her a cold, level stare. "Or do you take him directly to your bedroom? I've heard that's where you Washington career girls do a lot of your entertaining."

"Well, you should know," she shot back, remembering the intimate remarks that had passed between her husband and Vera Caldwell. "But I'm not in the habit of entertaining men in bed, and that includes you." She cast him a defiant glare and marched purposefully into her room where she yanked clothes from closets and drawers.

As she began to fold and stuff underwear into her large blue suitcase, a new concern presented itself.

On Monday she had to be in the office at nine o'clock. So much had happened that she'd forgotten momentarily about her job. But it was important to her and she didn't want to lose it. She dropped the slips she was holding into the open suitcase and went to the doorway where she confronted Matt once more. He was sprawled on the loveseat and looked totally at home. For some reason this made her even more irritated.

"What about my job?" she demanded. "I need to be back here Monday morning for work and my car is still in Frederick."

"Your car is being delivered to my town house. But don't worry about work," he drawled. "This is

53

our honeymoon, remember? Your boss is a friend of mine, so I'm sure if I tell him the situation, he'll give you a temporary leave of absence."

Kara began to protest, "But I have a lot to do. I've started a big project. . . ."

"Listen, I'm not without influence. I'll call Harry Simpson right now," he said, moving assuredly toward the phone. "Everything will be okay."

As Matt located her boss' telephone number in the D.C. directory and confidently began to dial the number, Kara again had the sensation of being swept away on a tide of events. She seemed to have no control over her life anymore. Decisions concerning her were now being made by others. She felt like a helpless, abandoned child. Not since her parents' death had she felt so much at the mercy of strangers. Her shoulders drooping, she turned back to her bedroom to complete her haphazard packing.

Minutes later Matt had finished his call and joined her in the bedroom.

"Well, that's all settled," he remarked brusquely. "You have at least a two-week leave of absence. And we can probably extend that if it's necessary." He bent down and effortlessly swung her heavy suitcases up from the floor.

"Let's get out of here," he commanded, turning toward the door. "We've got a lot to do yet." Kara followed helplessly behind him, casting a hasty farewell glance at her apartment before he closed the door firmly behind her.

On the drive north to Matt's town house in Columbia, they stopped for sandwiches at a deli. Matt, his brow furrowed in concentration, made no attempt at conversation. And Kara felt too depressed and beaten to attempt any more verbal sallies. But as they approached the entrance to the new city of Columbia, Matt looked at her inquiringly.

"Is this your first time here?" he asked.

"I've heard of it," she admitted, beginning to look around with interest, "but I've never been here." They were entering from the south. Trees lined the road on either side and handsome modern buildings swung into view.

"This is the downtown area," Matt explained. "You can't see it, but there's a man-made lake behind there," he pointed out.

"It's so spacious-looking for a downtown," Kara remarked, gazing around at the wide green lawns interspersed with patches of natural woods and beds of red and yellow tulips and daffodils. The whole effect was bright and clean, and Kara found herself admiring the new city that would be her temporary home.

A few minutes later Matt turned into a narrow drive leading to a small semicircle of starkly contemporary white town houses overlooking another lake.

"This is where we live," Matt commented smoothly, emphasizing the we.

"You mean this is where you live and where I'll be visiting," she retorted. His mouth tightened, and he gave her a dark, enigmatic look.

"Have it your way," he replied at last. "But I think you'll like it here." While he took her luggage out of the trunk, she opened the door and stepped out. Staring up at the elegant town house, she was suddenly afraid. Where would she spend the night? she wondered, and what kind of a night would it be?

But before she had an opportunity to ponder this question, she heard car doors open behind them, and shouts of "Mr. Jordan, Mrs. Jordan," greeted her ears.

Turning in surprise, she caught sight of a mass of reporters scrambling to get pictures and interviews with the newlywed couple. Cameras were clicking and grinding, and questions filled the air. As the reporters vied for her and Matt's attention, Kara looked wildly for an escape route. But Matt handled the situation expertly. Raising one hand, he called for silence.

"I'll answer all your questions inside," he said smoothly, "as soon as I've had an opportunity to get rid of these suitcases." Then Matt, looking cool and collected, headed toward the front door, Kara in tow, while the reporters followed behind.

When he'd opened the door and set the luggage inside, a voice cried out, "Aren't you going to carry the bride over the threshold?"

While the other reporters joined in the request, Matt gave Kara a hooded glance. A half-smile quirked the corners of his firm lips. In the next instant he had scooped her up and carried her into the spacious, high-ceilinged living room overlooking the lake.

"Welcome home, Mrs. Jordan," he whispered into her burning ears as he held her tightly. Then, setting her down on the polished parquet floor, he turned to meet the newsmen.

Cameras were grinding while reporters shot a barrage of questions at the candidate. Feeling nervous and foolish, Kara forced a tight smile while she listened to her husband field each volley like the practiced politician he was. Half an hour later he ushered the crowd of satisfied journalists out. The moment the door closed Kara collapsed on the couch and Matt settled his lean frame down beside her.

"I don't know how you endure this," Kara muttered, forcing a strand of hair out of her eyes. "It's like living in a fishbowl."

Matt leaned back on the couch and stretched his long legs. "It'll get worse before it gets better," he commented philosophically. "I'm a public servant and so I have to make myself available to the media. You can see why it's so important that my life be free of any hint of scandal just now."

Kara made a face and turned her head from him. "Yes, your image is so important that you don't care who you trample on to protect it. I've certainly learned *that* in the last few hours."

Matt was silent, seeming to turn her criticism over in his mind. He was preparing to say something to her when an antique grandfather clock in the corner chimed the half hour, distracting him.

"Heavens, it's four-thirty," he cried, clapping a hand on his forehead. "I've got to call my mother and tell her about this before she hears it on the six o'clock news!" He jumped up and strode toward his study adjoining the living room. As he disappeared behind the door, he tossed over his shoulder, "Why don't you amuse yourself by having a look around while I'm trying to explain this situation to her. You can unpack while you're at it, too."

"Not until I've found the guest bedroom," Kara

retorted. But he had already shut the door and left her alone. She stood up and walked to the center of the large, airy room. Through the sliding glass doors she could see a balcony, and beyond it the lake glittering in the late afternoon sun. The two sets of doors flanked a dramatic fireplace wall. Brown leather chairs and a Scandinavian area rug were arranged in a conversational grouping around the fireplace. A chrome and leather couch sat directly in front, facing a glass coffee table. A few prized antiques were mixed with the modern furniture to produce a pleasingly eclectic effect.

From there Kara drifted through the well-equipped kitchen and then up the stairs toward the bedrooms. A brown and white tweed carpet muffled her steps as she made her way to the second floor. Once in the hall, she peered through an open door on the right. She was obviously looking into the master bedroom. A huge king-size bed covered with a brown suede quilt dominated the large, skylit room. To one side stood a massive, mahogany dresser. Opposite, there was an armoire. An off-white shag rug covered the polished wood floor. Kara stood taking it all in for a moment and then turned quickly away. She had no intention of spending time in this particular room.

Across the hall she located a guest room. It was attractively decorated in shades of royal blue with cream walls. The furniture was sleekly modern, but the bed looked soft and comfortable. With a decisive nod of her dark head, Kara made her way back down the stairs to retrieve her suitcases. While she was busily unpacking, Matt suddenly appeared in the doorway, an ironic smile curling his lip as he watched.

Nervously she glanced up at him. His large, athlete's body seemed to fill the entire opening as he lounged indolently, one broad shoulder propped up against the wooden doorframe. His left leg was crossed easily, revealing the outline of his muscular thighs through the tautly stretched material of his jeans. Kara blinked and dragged her gaze away from his legs to look up once more at his face.

His narrowed gray eyes appraised her through a screen of lashes, and there was a thin smile on his well-molded mouth. As his glance skimmed slowly over her small, well-proportioned body, Kara had no trouble reading his mind. She felt vulnerable and powerless. How was she going to get through the next few weeks living with this arrogant, demanding man?

"I can see you're making yourself at home," he commented wryly. "There's far more closet space in my room across the hall, you know."

"The closet space here is quite adequate, thank you," she returned. Despite her efforts to make her voice cool and controlled, it came out sounding nervous and quavery. Turning her back to him, she bit her lip and busied herself arranging a wool skirt on a hanger.

"Just as you like," he replied carelessly, straightening up and moving away from the door. "I'll leave you alone so you can change for dinner. I've sent out for food. We can eat after the six o'clock news."

"The six o'clock news?" she questioned, folding a slip and placing it in a drawer.

"Yes, we'll probably be on it, and I'd like to see how our marriage act is playing." He moved away, closing the door gently behind him while Kara stared in consternation. What would the television reporters have to say about this hasty marriage and the reluctant politician's wife? she wondered. Kara looked at her watch. It was a quarter after five.

She took the next forty minutes unpacking and changing her clothes, deliberately stretching out the time so as not to confront the stranger she'd married that morning. Was it only that afternoon, she wondered as she pulled off her bridal blue jeans and searched through the clothes she'd brought for something else to wear. So much had happened in so short a time, she mused, as she rummaged through her drawer for her favorite beige sweater. When she'd found it, she pulled on brown corduroy slacks and a comfortable pair of moccasins.

She completed the outfit with a gold chain Wayne had bought her for her twenty-first birthday last year, smiling with satisfaction as it settled into place around her slender, white throat. Somehow the subtle act of defiance implied by wearing Wayne's gift made her feel more capable of dealing with Matt. She would not allow herself to be intimidated by the smooth-talking politician. She would deal with him just as she had dealt with politicians in the past. She would be the intelligent, capable woman she knew herself to be. With a proud lift of her head, she descended the stairs.

Once in the living room she looked around inquiringly. Matt was nowhere in sight, but she could hear the faint droning of the television from the other side of the room where his study door stood open. Taking a deep breath and squaring her shoulders, she strode purposefully across the wood floor and entered the booklined study. Matt was sprawled comfortably in a wine-red leather recliner watching a small color television set on a shelf above his huge walnut desk.

"Here, have a seat," he said, casually motioning her to the desk's wing chair which he had placed next to him. "I think the show's about to start."

Settling herself stiffly, Kara fixed her eyes on the television screen. When the anchorman's face appeared she waited anxiously to hear her name, but the top story was a fire at a chemical plant. While pictures of ambulances and firehoses lit up the screen, Kara watched the scenes of disaster float before her without really seeing them. Obsessed by her own situation, she could not concentrate on the reporter's words.

Her attention was quickly riveted to the screen, however, when the next story headline was "Maryland jet-setting politician marries political boss' niece!"

"With less than a month before the primary election, thirty-four-year-old congressional hopeful, Maryland jet-setter Matt Jordan surprised the press today by announcing his secret marriage to Kara Barnett, the niece of well-known Maryland political figure James Barnett," the anchorman enunciated smoothly. "Here for an on the spot account is our roving reporter Vera Caldwell."

The anchorman's suave visage disappeared from the screen to be replaced by a smiling, green-eyed Vera who wrapped her long manicured fingers around a hand-held mike. She was standing in front of Uncle James' cabin, smiling coyly.

"Matt Jordan's female constituents' hearts will be broken when they learn Maryland's most handsome state senator is no longer playing the field. Jordan has long been adored by every attractive woman in the state, and gossip columnists have speculated for years on who the lucky girl to wear his ring would be.

"In the past he's been linked with beautiful social-ites Linda Payton and Sandra 'Scoot' Townsend." Pictures of two glossily chic blondes illuminated the screen. Kara stared at them with narrowed eyes and shot a dark glance at Matt, who returned her look with a bland smile.

"But two days ago," the reporter continued, "Jordan put an end to the speculation by marrying the niece of top political boss James Barnett. People inside the party have expressed astonishment at his choice, but an unidentified source claims that the marriage was more a political maneuver than a love match, as Jordan had not been seen dating the twenty-two-year-old public relations specialist previous to their marriage."

Kara drew in her breath with sharp rage. The nerve of the woman, she fumed inwardly! But Matt, accustomed to such treatment, merely chuckled. Kara stared at the TV set while scenes of Matt and her uncle's press conference held earlier that day flickered across the screen. The two men pledged their intention to clean up state politics and solidify the party before the primary. Next came reaction from Matt's political opponent Bill Thorp, who barely commented on the official press conference and then derisively labeled the marriage as one of "political convenience."

Then suddenly the scene shifted, and the newly-weds were standing at the front entrance to Matt's town house. Smiling, the tall, darkly handsome politician scooped his bride up in his strong arms and carried her across the threshold.

The image projected was of a young, well-matched couple deeply in love. The scene was so convincing that Kara almost had to blink back tears from her deep violet eyes. What would it have been like, she wondered, if it had been a real marriage based on love rather than convenience? She looked down at her bare fingers twisted numbly in her lap and sighed, while Matt uncoiled his long limbs and strode across the room to turn off the television set.

"Well, that was pretty bad. But brace yourself, because if I know the press there'll be worse to come," he commented dryly, turning to face her.

A shiver ran up her spine while he stood towering over her, looking down. Again he seemed about to say something, but his attention was distracted by the sound of the doorbell.

"Not more reporters," he growled. Muttering a curse under his breath, he left the room to investigate. Kara sank back in the leather chair and closed her eyes. From the next room she could hear the sound of strange voices and the clatter of dishes. In a moment Matt reappeared in the doorway.

"It's only the caterer. Why don't we step out on the balcony while they set up dinner." He took her hand and led her out into the cool spring air.

Walking across the wide wooden deck, they leaned on the railing and looked out on the smooth

63

surface of the lake below. The sun was just beginning to set, sending fiery fingers of light across the cloud-lined sky.

"It's beautiful," Kara murmured, looking across the lake at budding, graceful willows and delicate ping magnolias in full bloom. "You must really enjoy living here."

"Yes, I particularly like having breakfast outside in the warm weather. But it will be nicer now that I'll have you sitting across the table from me."

Kara was silent. She doubted the marriage would last that long. But her musing was broken by squawking on the bike path below. Looking down she saw a female duck trying desperately to evade the determined attentions of a persistent drake. Attempting to elude her pursuer, the female rushed toward the false safety of a clump of bushes in the hopes of losing him, but the relentless drake cut off her escape. Seizing her neck roughly in his bill, he forced himself on her despite her loud cries of protest.

Matt smiled at his new bride provocatively. "Now there's a male who knows how to handle a woman," he murmured huskily. One of his large hands grasped the back of Kara's slender neck and turned her heart-shaped face toward him. For a moment he stood looking down at her while she felt herself barely breathing. The moment seemed to stretch out forever—but just as Matt bent his dark head down to kiss her, the caterer poked his face through the patio doorway and announced that dinner was ready.

Matt had ordered a hearty beef burgundy entrée served with parsley potatoes and a crisp spinach salad. Dessert was chocolate mousse.

During dinner the conversation remained light. They talked about the latest movies they'd seen and the restaurants in Washington that they had enjoyed. And they discovered that they shared a mutual passion for the French impressionistic art at the National Gallery.

"If you like what they have there, I'll have to show you the collection at the Jeu de Paume in Paris," Matt said warmly, refilling her wine glass.

Much to her surprise, Kara found her new husband easy to talk to. And as the meal drew to a close, she was feeling relaxed and almost cheerful.

But as they picked up the dishes to take them to the kitchen, Matt's eyes lingered on the necklace at her throat. During the meal she had noticed him glance at it several times speculatively.

"That's quite a fancy necklace," he commented as he placed the dishes on the brown ceramic tile counter top.

Kara licked her lips. She wished she hadn't worn Wayne's gift. "Thank you," she replied, nervously fingering the links. "It was a present."

Matt's eyes narrowed and his mouth hardened. "A gift from whom?" he demanded.

She avoided his penetrating glance while she sought for an evasive answer. "Just a friend," she stammered.

"Your good friend Wayne?" he insisted suspiciously. She didn't reply. But the heightened color in her cheeks gave him the answer.

"I don't want you wearing presents from other men now that you're my wife. Please remove it." Although his voice was quiet, it held a note of demand that Kara resented.

"That's ridiculous," she countered, turning away to put her dishes in the sink. "I like this necklace. And if I want to wear it, I will."

Suddenly she felt his presence directly behind her, then strong fingers were at the clasp of the delicate chain. She felt the metal slide against her skin and the slow, sensual movement of Matt's mouth caress the sensitive spot at the back of her neck where the chain had been. His hands touched her arms, sliding silkily down them, the brush of his long fingers making her skin burn with awareness. And then his hand casually deposited the chain on the counter top.

Trembling with a mixture of anger and arousal, Kara tried to move away. But his hands shot out, closing around her waist and pulling her hard against him so that she felt the tense virility of his body pressed behind her. His mouth touched the nape of her neck again.

"If you want jewelry," he whispered, his breath hot in her ear while his hard thighs held her prisoner against the counter, "I'll buy it for you." And with that he brushed the offending chain off the counter top and into the garbage.

Shocked, Kara jerked herself free and spun around to stare at him in disbelief. "How dare you! What gives you the right to do that?" she flared.

Without waiting for a reply she retrieved the chain, turned on her heels and headed for the stairs.

"So that's the kind of man you are, Matt Jordan," she tossed back over her shoulder. Running to the safety of the guest bedroom, Kara slammed and locked the door.

Then she tried to calm herself. "I'm not going to

let that, that . . . that man get to me," she insisted, trying to be as rational as possible. "He's not worth it. And the sooner I can get out of this crazy marriage, the better."

Kara looked around the room and sighed. The clock on the bedside table said nine o'clock. It was definitely the longest day of her life, and probably the most confused. She looked longingly at the bed, wanting nothing more than to crawl under the covers and go to sleep. But she knew that she was still too upset to think of sleeping.

Maybe what I need first is a hot bath, she told herself. Kara rummaged through the closet and drawers she'd just filled for her ivory brushed-nylon robe and a modest gown. After getting undressed and folding her clothing neatly on the chair, she carried the nightclothes and some hairpins into the bathroom.

"My gosh, this looks like something out of *House Beautiful*," she muttered as she eyed the airy, white tiled room with its oversized sunken tub and expansive skylight. Floor to ceiling mirror panels covered the far wall. A large potted plant was tucked in a corner, and hanging baskets of lush, green ferns lent an exotic air.

Then Kara pinned up her raven curls. As she bent over the gleaming ivory tub to turn on the gilded faucets, her eye caught a glimpse of a crystal bottle filled with pink liquid. Upon closer inspection, she realized that it was bath oil and automatically began pouring some into the stream of hot water. But as the scent of peach blossoms filled the room, she set the bottle down hard on the edge of the tub.

This is a woman's scent, she thought angrily—who

had used it? A picture of the redheaded Vera popped into her mind. Was she the peach blossom type? Or had it been someone else? And what about the size of the tub? It was big enough for two. Was this one of Matt's playrooms?

All right, Kara, she told herself. Stop it. Whatever Matt's done is nothing to you. Don't let him upset you again. Determinedly she stepped into the scented water and settled her delicate body into its inviting warmth.

She closed her eyes, letting the soothing vapor of the bath float away her tension.

Ah, that's better, she thought, sinking a little lower into the water and putting her head back against the sloping end of the tub. But she had been relaxing for only a few minutes when she was disturbed by the sound of a door latch clicking. Startled, she opened her eyes to be greeted by the horrifying sight of the mirror panels sliding open. Matt Jordan emerged wearing only a short silk robe.

"I heard your tub water running. It sounded so inviting I thought I'd join you," he drawled.

"It wasn't an invitation," Kara spat out between clenched teeth, her eyes blazing.

But he ignored her outburst, his eyes lingering on the glimmering white curves of her body enticingly visible beneath the surface of the steamy water.

Hotly conscious of his sensual appraisal, Kara sank deeper in the tub, her fury now mixed with fear. "Get out of here," she cried. "You have no right to be in here!"

"On the contrary," he retorted. "I have every right. This is my house and you are my wife. It's time we cleaned up our act," he said, grinning as he

68

sauntered across the room toward the tub. Bending slowly next to the steamy water, he leaned over and whispered in her ear, "This is our wedding night, you know. And I've been looking forward to celebrating it properly all day. I wouldn't have married you if that weren't part of the bargain."

"What do you mean?" Kara quavered, locking her arms protectively across her breasts. "I thought we had agreed that this was going to be a platonic arrangement." Despite herself she had to drag her eyes away from the tanned, muscular legs visible beneath the short robe.

"That was your idea, it was never mine. I'm a doer, not a dreamer. That's part of my campaign slogan," he chuckled.

Before Kara could reply, Matt's hand slipped into the warm water and playfully began to ripple the surface of the bath, sending tiny waves splashing against her breasts. Kara felt her face turn red as her flesh tingled. But she had no intention of responding to the pleasurable sensation and quickly moved to the other side of the tub out of Matt's reach.

"Making room for me?" he mocked, beginning to untie the cord of his robe.

Kara gasped. He obviously meant to join her in the water. She could feel her anger rising. The nerve of the man! Not only had he maneuvered her into an unwanted marriage and messed up her job, he was now planning on using her like all the other easy women in his life. She wanted no part of his plans and she wanted to make sure he got the message. She would douse his passions in a tangible way he wouldn't soon forget!

Her calculating eyes lit on the hand-held shower

attachment next to the water faucets. Scooting forward, she grabbed the attachment with her right hand, aimed it at Matt, and turned the cold water on full with her left.

About to pull off his robe, he was hit full in the abdomen by the cold needle-sharp spray. He shouted in astonishment, but his surprise quickly turned to anger.

"Why, you little witch," he exclaimed, reaching over and trying to wrest the spray from her hand. But Kara held on with determination and the nozzle careened wildly, spraying the bathroom with icy water.

Before he was able to take the shower attachment away from her and turn it off, Matt was drenched and Kara's hair was dripping. Matt grabbed Kara by the shoulders, pulled her out of the tub and shoved a towel at her. "That was a juvenile trick," he grated. "If you'd simply asked me to leave with real conviction in your voice I would have. But children who like to play games have to learn to clean up the mess they make." Turning on his heels, he stalked out.

Dripping and cold, Kara stared furiously at his disappearing back. He was insufferable, and she cursed the fate that had sent her up to Uncle James' cabin. But a nagging doubt kept tugging at her conscience. Was he right? Had she handled the situation badly?

Her anger was stronger than any feeling of remorse, though. If he thinks I'm going to clean this up, he's crazy, she told herself. Let it dry by itself! Pulling on her robe, she stamped out of the room.

It was while she was toweling herself dry in the bedroom that she heard the phone ringing shrilly on the extension at the bedside table. Kara picked it up and was about to say, "Jordan's residence," when she heard a husky female voice whisper, "Matt, is that you?"

"Yes," she heard her husband answer.

"You've got to come over right away, I need you," the woman went on, her voice thick with emotion.

Silently Kara replaced the phone on its cradle. She sat down on the bed and waited coldly to see what would happen. A few minutes later she heard her husband's muffled footsteps on the carpeted stairs, and then the click of the front door opening and closing.

Tears filled her eyes. He was spending their wedding night in the arms of another woman. She knew she shouldn't care. But, to her horror, she realized that she did.

Chapter Five

The golden rays of sunlight streaming in the sliding glass door to the balcony awoke Kara. The warmth of the sun felt good against her bare arms, and she stretched lazily before her eyes focused on the unfamiliar bedroom surroundings. Suddenly it all came back—the forced wedding, the farce they had seen on the evening news, and the scene in the bathroom before Matt had rushed out to his late night assignation.

That *must* have been Vera on the phone, she thought, her blood running cold despite the warmth of the sun. Matt couldn't even stay away from her on our wedding night. But another dark thought crossed her mind. If Vera hadn't called, what would have happened? Would Matt have tried to force his way into her bedroom? she wondered.

Kara shuddered. But the shiver that went through

her body reminded her of the disturbingly pleasurable sensations she had felt when Matt's eyes had traveled over her body, mirroring his desire. What would it have been like if this were a real marriage? she wondered. It would have been all right then to respond to a husband's exploring caresses. And he would have had no reason to leave his wife on their marriage night and seek out the comfort of his mistress.

But this line of reasoning was getting Kara nowhere. This isn't a real marriage, she reminded herself sternly. I don't want it to be. And I know Matt doesn't either. So there's no use considering what might have happened.

And with that thought, she swung her legs out of bed and pulled on the dressing gown she had folded over the back of the chair the night before. The thick shag carpet felt good under her bare feet as she crossed to the adjoining bathroom. Opening the door, she looked around the room. The water on the floor had dried, leaving no evidence of the previous night's battle.

This time I'm not going to let Matt Jordan surprise me in here, she muttered aloud, inspecting the mirrored panel and finding a latch at the top to hold it closed. But as her fingers reached for the fastening, she couldn't help giving way to an impulse to quietly open the door and peek into his bedroom.

The room was empty and the neatly made bed proclaimed that no one had slept there last night.

Why, he must have been out all night, she fumed. With that she quickly slid back the panel and turned purposefully toward the sink.

After making her toilet and pulling her hair back

into a simple pony tail, Kara returned to her bedroom and pulled on her oldest pair of faded jeans and a frayed yellow T-shirt with the legend "Maryland is for Crabs" printed on the front over the picture of a large red crustacean. She'd picked up the shirt on a Chesapeake Bay sailing expedition several years ago. But now she rarely wore it unless she was planning to wash her car. She completed the outfit with a worn pair of jogging shoes. And then headed downstairs toward the kitchen. What she needed was a cup of coffee, she thought.

All of the draperies on the lower floor were drawn. And the house seemed unusually quiet as Kara strode across the living room. But as she opened the cafe doors into the kitchen, she was surprised by the aroma of freshly made coffee and the sight of her husband sitting at the round butcher block table reading the financial section of the *Baltimore Sun*. He was dressed in flannel gray slacks, a creamy beige turtleneck, and a casual tweed sportscoat with leather patches at the elbows. The sight of Matt looking so cool and unruffled after their stormy encounter of the night before enraged her.

"Well, sleeping beauty is finally awake," he observed mockingly. Then his eyes roamed over her scruffy outfit. "Or is it the scullery maid?"

Kara tried to think of a snappy comeback. But none came to mind.

"By the way," Matt added, "the message on the T-shirt is superfluous. You've already made it clear what a crab you can be. But you'd better hide your claws for today. We're going out to Windy Willow Farm to meet my mother."

74

Kara's mouth flew open. "We are? Why didn't you have the courtesy to tell me? But then, why should I expect courtesy from someone like you?"

"If you hadn't made it clear that you didn't want my company last night, we might have had more time to discuss our plans for today," he retorted, studying her coldly.

"You mean, if you hadn't been in such a hurry to get out of here and into bed with your mistress," she countered.

Matt Jordan threw back his head and laughed at her accusations. "And just what makes you think that?" he challenged.

"I happened to pick up the phone in my bedroom and I heard . . ." Kara began.

But the dangerous glint in her husband's eyes cut her off in mid-sentence.

"I will not tolerate anyone eavesdropping on my conversations," he said very calmly and deliberately. But the icy tone of his voice sent a shiver up Kara's spine. Biting her lip, she looked down at the table top.

"And since you've made it clear that you don't really want to be my wife, where I go and what I do is really no concern of yours."

Kara felt her lower lip begin to quiver. And she was unable to look up and meet his eyes. But the next second he reached out and covered her long slender fingers with his strong hand.

"You don't know how I spent last night, Kara," he said more gently. "And if you did, you'd understand that I have good reason to be edgy this morning. But we have a long day ahead of us at my mother's place in the country, so let's call a truce. I'll heat up some blueberry muffins for breakfast while you go up and change into something more suitable for meeting her. And for heaven's sakes, take your hair out of that pony tail. She'll think I'm robbing the cradle."

Still unable to look up, Kara turned and fled from the kitchen. Back in her bedroom she looked through her closets and drawers trying to find something that Matt would consider suitable for a visit to Windy Willow Farms. Finally she settled on a burgundy corduroy skirt with a matching vest and striped blouse. To add a note of sophistication, she pulled on a pair of high-heeled, brown suede boots. Then she brushed out her hair, put on a dab of lip gloss and a touch of violet eye shadow.

"What am I doing?" she asked herself suddenly as she surveyed her image in the mirror. "I don't want to go meet his mother. How can I act as if things are normal when this whole affair has been so contrived? I'm going to tell him I won't go," she said decisively.

When she returned to the kitchen, Matt surveyed her assessingly. "That's a lot better," he approved, "although you're still not quite sophisticated enough to play the part of a candidate's wife. But we'll talk about that later."

"You certainly know how to give a woman compliments," Kara observed caustically, pulling out a pedestal chair and sitting down at the table. Then she reached for the butter and a hot muffin. "But I'm not going with you," she declared.

"And just why not?" he countered, his eyes narrowing.

"Because after last night, it would be hypocritical if I were to play the dutiful bride to your loving husband."

"Now get this straight, Kara. No matter what you think of me, you have an obligation to go through with our bargain; and meeting my mother in a civil fashion is part of that." The no-nonsense expression on Matt's hard features was so intimidating that Kara found herself once again avoiding his gaze.

They sat in silence for some minutes, each concentrating on the breakfast in front of them. Finally, feeling Matt's eyes on her, Kara looked up to find an unreadable expression on his face.

"Remember, we're supposed to be having a truce," he reminded her. "And here's my first peace offering," he said, with a more friendly expression. Reaching into his pocket, he pulled out a small velvet box and put it on the table in front of Kara's plate. "Go ahead and open it," he urged.

Tentatively, Kara picked it up and slowly pulled back the lid. Inside a wedding ring set sparkled. The engagement ring was a large marquis diamond flanked by six smaller emeralds. The wedding band was a narrow circle of gold. Involuntarily, Kara drew in her breath.

"They're beautiful," she murmured.

"I hope this makes up for yesterday," her husband said softly. Reaching out he took her left hand and slipped the two rings on the proper finger. Just as before, the fit was perfect.

"This time you don't have to give them back," he chuckled.

"You mean, even when we get divorced," she blurted.

His gray eyes became hard as granite. "Just as you wish," he said coolly. "But as long as you're playing the candidate's wife, you'll wear them." Then he

77

pushed back his chair and stood up. "Are you coming?" he asked.

Kara nodded dumbly.

"Well then, I hate to rush you through breakfast, but Mother's expecting us at eleven."

During most of the twenty-minute ride to Windy Willow Farm, Kara purposely kept her eyes averted from Matt, even though she was acutely aware of his magnetic presence, especially when his hand brushed lightly against her leg as he changed gears. She tried to concentrate on the fluffy white clouds scudding across the crystal blue of the sky and the rolling hills divided like patchwork by white rail fences and rows of blooming dogwood. But her thoughts were in turmoil. What would his mother be like? What would she think about Kara and this hasty marriage?

As they turned onto the gravel entrance road to the estate, she could remain silent no longer.

"What are we going to tell your mother?" she blurted.

"We're going to tell her the truth. I'm not going to insult her with the charade we've made up for the public."

"But what will she think of me?" Kara pressed.

Matt flashed her a narrowed look. "My mother's very open-minded. I'm sure that will depend on the way you behave yourself today."

Kara flushed. "I don't have anything against your mother," she protested indignantly.

"Other than that I'm her son," he added dryly.

Agreeing with him silently, Kara turned her attention to the scene out the window. The Jordan estate was impressive, she had to admit.

The winding driveway was flanked by a row of willow trees, feathered with the delicate greenery of their first spring growth. To the right was a large oval pond in which a flock of mallards had made themselves at home. To the left were acres of white fenced paddocks where thoroughbred mares and their new foals grazed peacefully.

At the end of the long drive was a two story fieldstone house with high white portico stretching across the front expanse. Ancient boxwood hedges lined the flagstone walk. And beds of lemon-tinted daffodils and bright red tulips provided a splash of color in front of the stately structure.

"When you said Windy Willow Farm, I had no idea it was this impressive," Kara accused. "You could have prepared me."

Next to her, Matt grinned. "I never thought of it that way. This is where I grew up," he said warmly. "It's just home to me."

Matt parked the silver Porsche at the edge of the circular drive in front of the house. Getting out, he walked around to Kara's side of the car, opened the door, and took her arm. Even after he shut the door behind her, he held onto her tightly as he led her up the walk.

When they were almost to the house, the front door flew open and a tall, slim, white-haired man dressed in a work shirt, jeans and leather riding boots emerged.

"Welcome home, Matt," he boomed. "Your mother is as excited as a high-strung filly over your marriage." Then he turned to Kara.

"So this is the lucky bride," he chuckled approvingly. "We didn't think anybody was going to lasso

79

our Matt. But honey, I want to tell you you've got one heck of a man here."

The color in Kara's cheeks heightened. But Matt handled the situation smoothly.

"I'd like you to meet Lew McAlister," he said. "Lew's been with the family since before I was born. He runs the horse farm for my mother. He's quite a character with his Wild West ways, but you don't have to believe everything he says."

"I'm . . . I'm pleased to meet you," Kara stammered, holding out her hand. But McAlister swept her into a bear hug. "I expect you to take good care of this boy," he drawled in her ear. "But I'll let you in on a secret; it takes a tight rein to keep him out of trouble. I know, I had the job for twenty years."

"You don't want to frighten her off, do you Lew?" Matt asked dryly.

"You're right. I better stop flapping my mouth. And you better go in to see your mother," he said to Matt.

But before he turned toward the paddocks, he winked at Kara.

Matt opened the door and they stepped into the cool, elegant foyer. The floor was black and white marble tile, set off with oriental rugs. A curving staircase with an elaborately carved railing swept up to the second floor. And the long Chippendale hall table held a polished silver bowl brimming with an arrangement of freshly cut spring flowers. Matt steered Kara down the hall toward the back of the house. As Kara passed the living room and dining room, she had a quick impression of expensive antique furniture and plush upholstery.

"This is like the Sugar Hill mansion I toured once in Philadelphia when I was in college," she whispered.

"Well, this one's not open to the public all the time, but it is included on the Christmas candlelight tours my mother organizes each year for Maryland charities. But let's not keep her waiting; she's probably in the greenhouse."

At the back of the house they entered a large glassed-in room where the air was heady with the smell of flowers and plants. In the middle of the room Kara could see an elegant-looking silver-haired woman dressed in a pale blue shirtwaist who was busy repotting an enormous Boston fern. As they entered, the woman looked up and a warm smile spread across her aristocratic features.

"Matthew dear," she said, standing up and stripping off her gardening gloves. "And this must be Kara." She hurried forward and gave the young woman an affectionate embrace. "I can't tell you how happy I am to welcome you to the family."

Kara found herself responding to the genuine warmth of this woman who seemed so different from her overbearing son. But she didn't know what to say. Over Mrs. Jordan's shoulder, she looked at Matt helplessly, her eyes begging him to explain the situation.

"Mother, there's something I have to tell you," Matt began.

But Mrs. Jordan, who had stepped back from Kara, shook her head. "You don't have to tell me anything," she interrupted. "Frank Adams was here yesterday afternoon and explained the whole story."

81

Matt's features hardened. "Then he's overstepped his responsibilities," he ground out. "His duties don't extend to my personal life."

"That may be true," his mother agreed. "But I'm grateful he did. I've already had several phone calls from the media asking for my reaction. I'm glad I had a better understanding of the situation."

Matt nodded tightly. "From that point of view, I guess it was appropriate," he relented.

His mother smiled. "Now, I'm not trying to get rid of you, Matt," she said, changing the subject. "But I do need your opinion on a horse sale Lew is taking care of for me tomorrow. Do you think you can go look at those yearlings and make sure he's set a fair asking price?"

"Mother, Lew knows a lot more about the correct price than I do," Matt protested.

But Mrs. Jordan made a swishing motion with her hands. "You run along and give me a chance to get to know Kara a little better," she laughed. Turning to the young woman, she added, "I never could put one over on him."

Matt gave them both an exaggerated shrug and headed out of the room.

"Now come into the family room and sit down," Mrs. Jordan said, turning to Kara. "I had that wing added several years ago. The original house was built before the Civil War."

Obediently, Kara followed the older woman down a short hallway.

Mrs. Jordan was still rattling on. "And my dear, you must call me Elizabeth. We don't stand on formalities around here."

The family room was comfortably furnished with a

beige velvet sectional sofa making a U in front of the brick fireplace. The coffee and end tables were of chrome and glass. And one wall was lined with fruitwood cabinets topped by ceiling-high bookshelves.

Mrs. Jordan gestured for Kara to sit on the left side of the sofa, as she crossed to one of the bookshelves and took down a large oatmeal-colored volume with blue lettering.

"After Frank Adams left, your name jogged my memory," the older woman told Kara as she came to sit beside her on the couch. "So I got out my old college yearbook and had a look at it."

Kara gazed at her expectantly.

"Do you know your mother and I were classmates at Goucher College over thirty-six years ago? And you look so much like her, I feel as if I've known you a long time already."

Kara stared at her mother-in-law in surprise.

"You mean you really knew my mother, Mrs. Jordan?" she questioned.

"Yes. And I do want you to call me Elizabeth the way she did." While the elder Mrs. Jordan was talking, she flipped the pages of the yearbook. "See, here I am," she pointed to a youthful version of herself. "And here's your mother."

"Oh, you were Elizabeth Remington. Why, I've looked at my mother's yearbook dozens of times. But of course I never knew who you were," Kara exclaimed.

Elizabeth Jordan patted the young woman's hand. "I know how much your mother meant to you, Kara," she said gently. "She was a wonderful person. And I was just sick when I heard about the plane crash that took her and your father. We had lost track of each other soon after she got married, and I didn't even know that she had a daughter until yesterday."

Kara nodded numbly.

"I know she would have been so proud of you. Frank Adams tells me you're a public relations specialist. Did you know your mother had a promising career as a journalist before she got married? She made much better use of her education than I did. I got married right after graduation and had Matt ten months later."

Kara studied Mrs. Jordan. Here was a woman who seemed to know more about her mother than she herself did. Maybe this explained why she felt so comfortable and secure with Matt's mother.

"We'll have to reminisce sometime soon," Mrs. Jordan promised. "But right now I want to talk about you and Matt."

Kara felt herself growing tense. How could she talk to Matt's mother about the confusing swirl of events that had swept her up into this crazy marriage?

But Mrs. Jordan seemed unaware or unwilling to acknowledge her distress.

"My philosophy is that everything always turns out for the best, Kara. And even though this marriage had a rather unusual beginning, I'm sure that you and Matt will be able to work things out."

Kara shook her head. "I don't think Matt wants to work things out. He's difficult to understand."

"Well, I know my son," the older woman insisted. "I don't think he would have married you unless he wanted to. He's never let himself be railroaded into anything he was dead set against. And I know with my mother's instinct that you're not indifferent to him either."

Kara opened her mouth to deny this, but she couldn't find the words. She knew she was physically attracted to Matt—more attracted than she had been to any man before—but could it be more than that? And what about Matt? What did he really feel for her? She knew he wanted to take her to bed. But did he feel anything besides lust for her? she wondered.

"I know this is a difficult way for you to start married life, Kara," Mrs. Jordan told her. "It's going to be hard for you and hard for Matt too, because he's always been so independent. But if he had to get into this kind of situation, I'm glad it's with a girl like you. And I want you to know that I'm your friend, and I'll be here if you need me."

The women had become so absorbed in their conversation that they were not aware that Matt was standing in the doorway.

"Defecting to the enemy camp already, Mother?" he asked wryly.

At the sound of his voice Kara jumped. But Mrs. Jordan dismissed his remark with a smile.

"Nonsense, Matthew, there are no enemies here. Now why don't you show Kara around the farm for a little while and I'll see how brunch is coming. Maybe half an hour's walk around the estate in this gorgeous spring weather will perk up your appetites."

Mrs. Jordan got up and strode from the room, leaving Matt and Kara staring at each other warily.

It was he who finally broke the silence. "As you may have noticed," he said lightly, "Mother's word here at Windy Willow Farm is law. So let me show you around the place. We can start with the paddocks."

Matt led Kara through the sliding glass doors in the family room onto a huge patio covered with a yellow canvas awning. From there they took a winding flagstone path toward the paddocks.

"How many horses does your mother have?" Kara inquired.

"About thirty now, but we'll be selling half a dozen yearlings over the next few months. Quite a few of mother's horses have racing potential, you know. In fact, Maryland Dancer, who's running in the Preakness next month, was one of our foals.

"Does your mother train racing horses?" Kara asked with interest.

"No, she just raises them."

They stopped by a white fence to admire several young colts and fillies grazing inside.

"Too bad I didn't bring some sugar," Matt observed. "I guess I just don't come back here often enough anymore."

Kara glanced at her husband. He seemed so much more relaxed and approachable in this setting. Looking over at her he grinned and grabbed her hand.

"Let's go down to the barn. I used to work there every day after school helping Lew and his men."

He started off at a brisk walk. And Kara had to run to keep up with his long strides. As Matt pulled the heavy barn door open, the hinges squeaked protestingly.

"Can't understand why one of the hands hasn't fixed that," he observed, looking around the barn.

But there was no one inside and no horses in the spacious stalls. Matt led Kara to a ladder near one wall.

"Come on up to the hayloft," he invited playfully. "I used to fool around up here all the time when I didn't want to do my homework. But Lew always knew where to find me."

Kara looked doubtfully at the ladder. But Matt had already started to climb. If she stayed down on the ground he would probably think her a bad sport. So she grasped the wooden bars and began to climb.

When she got to the top of the ladder, Matt was waiting. He took her hand and helped her up through the opening in the ceiling.

"Let me show you the view," he urged. Releasing a latch on a trapdoor in the wall, he pulled it open to reveal a panoramic scene of the pastures below.

In her high-heeled boots, Kara found it hard to walk in the deep straw. As she moved toward the opening, the heel of her left foot caught in one of the rafters and she pitched forward.

Matt's arm shot out to catch her, but her weight sent him off balance and the two of them fell over into the soft, dry hay.

Kara sat up and started to brush herself off. "Your mother will think we've been tumbling up here," she giggled.

"That's not a bad idea," Matt drawled, pulling her back down against him in the soft bed of loose straw. No longer laughing, Kara tried to push him away. But the strong band of his arms only pulled her into a more intimate position.

"As long as we're going to be found guilty anyway, we might as well commit the crime," he murmured, his lips feathering light kisses on her face.

"No. What if somebody finds us here?" Kara argued. But Matt silenced her protest with a hard, demanding kiss. She felt her lips part as his tongue made daring exploration of her mouth.

Against her will a wild excitement was growing within her and she slid her arms around his waist, pulling her pliant body against his taut muscles. His lips were on her hair, her face, her neck, sending shivers up her spine. Then his hands tugged free her blouse from the waist band of her skirt. She felt strong fingers caressing the sensitive skin of her back, trailing little darts of pleasure across her flesh. Then, in one fluid motion, he had unhooked her bra. His hands slid around to the front to cup her breasts and her nipples hardened at his exploration.

"Oh, Matt," she moaned, lost in the swirl of overpowering sensations he was creating. His insistent hands and mouth were shaping her body to his will. She was under his control. He could do with her what he wished. All thoughts of the real reason for this marriage had been banished by his drugging caresses. The only thing that existed was this moment and a deep aching need within her.

From somewhere far away she heard the squeaking of hinges. At the sound Matt pulled away from her and sat up alertly. Below them, the voice of Lew McAlister drifted up toward the hayloft.

"I know you're up there Matt. It doesn't take a genius to figure out the first place you'd take Kara was where you used to initiate all your old girlfriends to farm life."

"Get lost, Lew," Matt rasped. "We'll be down in a minute."

Kara could hear Lew chuckling as he sauntered out. She sat up. The situation held no humor for her. Outrage flashed in her violet eyes.

"So, I'm just another one of your rolls in the hay," she accused vehemently, as she tried to pull her clothing back in order.

Matt didn't answer.

"Lew has a really poor sense of timing," he observed, brushing hay from his own clothes. "Maybe he's forgotten we're on our honeymoon," he added.

"But I haven't forgotten why we got married," Kara shot back.

"Oh yes you did," her husband corrected. "Don't deny it. Your body told me you wanted me just as much as I wanted you."

Brusquely Kara turned away from him and started down the ladder. It was a somber pair of newlyweds who made their way back to the main house. But when they reached the side door, Matt put his hand on Kara's arm.

"There's a powder room right inside here," he gestured. "You can repair the damage to your appearance there."

Kara nodded, knowing full well she could never repair the damage her self-esteem had just suffered.

A few minutes later she joined Matt and Mrs. Jordan in the dining room. A sumptuous buffet of country ham, scrambled eggs, apple fritters, cinnamon buns and fresh strawberries was spread out on the sideboard along with silver pots of tea and coffee.

"I thought we could serve ourselves," Mrs. Jordan told Kara, "since I like to give the servants an early day on Sunday."

Kara watched Matt fill his plate and pour a cup of coffee. But she had lost her appetite and only took enough to be polite.

However, Mrs. Jordan seemed not to notice the strained atmosphere.

"I've been thinking," she said, when she had brought her own plate and cup to the table. "We should have a wedding reception for the two of you very soon."

"A wedding reception?" Kara was stunned.

"Why yes, my dear, there will be enough speculation about your marriage as it is. We must do things properly and introduce you to all our friends at a formal reception."

"Is that necessary, Mother?" Matt asked.

"Politically, I think it is," Mrs. Jordan assured him. "And besides, all our friends would feel very hurt if we don't have them over to meet Kara."

Matt nodded. "I suppose you're right," he agreed. "But we will have to find something suitable for Kara to wear."

Kara's violet eyes flashed. She was about to make a scathing retort to Matt, but he shot her a warning glance.

Mrs. Jordan leaped into the conversational breach.

"Now Matt, I'm sure there's nothing wrong with Kara's taste in clothing," she soothed. "Her wardrobe just doesn't reflect her new position." She turned to Kara and continued. "If you'd permit me, I'm sure it would be loads of fun for the two of us to go on a shopping trip to Bethesda together. I'd love to help you spend some of Matt's money at I. Magnin's and Bloomingdales."

Mrs. Jordan's smile was so warm that Kara found herself smiling in return.

"When do you want to go?" Kara asked.

"The sooner the better, my dear. How about tomorrow? I'll want to get the invitations printed for the reception, too. We can have it in, let's see, a week."

"A week? But that's so soon," Kara gasped.

"The sooner we introduce you as Matt's wife, the better it will be for his candidacy," Mrs. Jordan said reassuringly. Then she pushed back her chair and went to the sideboard for another cup of coffee. The subject was apparently closed.

Chapter Six

The next morning Mrs. Jordan's chauffeur-driven limousine deposited her and Kara at the main entrance of White Flint Mall. This was Kara's first visit to the posh three-story shopping center with its glass enclosed elevators and indoor gardens flanked by ceramic tile walkways.

She looked about her with interest at the enticing store displays featuring everything from expensive chess sets, with pieces decked out like lords and ladies at a medieval court, to antique oriental porcelain bowls, fine jewelry and designer lingerie.

"Would you like a cup of coffee and a croissant first?" Mrs. Jordan asked, steering Kara toward an indoor sidewalk cafe with old-fashioned wire frame chairs and brightly polished square copper table tops. "They have such marvelous blends here."

"That sounds terrific," Kara agreed enthusiastically, pulling out a chair and sitting down. "I didn't have much for breakfast."

"I think I'll have the Viennese coffee," Mrs. Jordan told the waitress.

Kara selected a Mocha Java blend to drink with her buttery croissant. When the waitress had left, Mrs. Jordan turned to her daughter-in-law.

"Now, it's really none of my business," she began. "But I did notice a certain strain in the relationship between you and Matt at brunch yesterday."

Flustered, Kara took a sip of her coffee and touched her lips with her napkin. How would she respond to the older woman's remark? Finally she said, "I'm having trouble sorting out my feelings toward Matt. One minute we're getting along fine. But the next minute, we're at each other's throats. I don't know how he really feels about our marriage."

Mrs. Jordan reached over and covered Kara's hand with her own. "I think I know how you feel, my dear," she sympathized. "Ever since Matt's father died, when he was ten, he's kept his emotions locked tightly inside himself. Even I often have trouble knowing what he's really feeling. And then there's Lew. He's had a lot to do with Matt's upbringing, because I felt he needed a strong man's hand. But maybe it was a bit too strong. Lew isn't one to display the tender emotions. But I think it's important to repeat what I said yesterday. Matt's his own man and he'd never let himself be trapped into a situation that he didn't really want. If he went to the extreme of marrying you, you must be special to him."

Kara looked at her mother-in-law doubtfully. "I wish I could really let myself believe you. But I feel so vulnerable," she murmured, shaking her head and setting down her coffee cup. "I just don't know whether or not our marriage has a future."

"I think that time will straighten things out," Mrs. Jordan reassured. "And the two of you have had so little time together."

Then she glanced at her watch. "But speaking of time, we are going to have to get on with the business at hand if we're going to meet Matt for an early dinner. Where shall we begin our shopping expedition?" she asked briskly, taking a last sip of coffee before putting down her cup. "I think I'll take you to see Joyce at this end of the mall first," she said, not waiting for an answer. "She always seems to have just what I'm looking for."

Mrs. Jordan's remark conjured up the image of a bustling, helpful saleslady. It in no way prepared Kara for the reality of Joyce, the haughtily sophisticated grande dame of one of Bethesda's most exclusive department store salons.

The salon itself was like nowhere else Kara had ever shopped. There were no displays of clothes or racks of dresses. Instead, Kara and Mrs. Jordan took their seats on red velvet-covered Victorian couches at one side of the elegantly decorated room. Overwhelmed by the atmosphere, the young woman glanced nervously at her mother-in-law. But Mrs. Jordan seemed in complete control of the situation.

"We need a complete wardrobe for my new daughter-in-law," she told Joyce. The tall angular woman, who was dressed in a silk designer suit with her hair swept into a French twist, listened attentively.

"We want to suggest a young, vibrant wife. Nothing too conservative. But not too flashy either," Mrs. Jordan went on.

Joyce eyed Kara speculatively, taking in her beige pants suit. "With your coloring you can wear either the pastels or the bright colors," she told the young woman. "But I think you'll have a more romantic image in the pastels. Let me go and make some selections."

A few minutes later Joyce, followed by a model, stepped through the curtained doorway at one side of the room. The model was wearing a light blue linen suit dress. Its simple lines bespoke its expensive price.

"Oh, that's lovely," Kara exclaimed. "But how much does it cost?"

"Now don't worry about that," Mrs. Jordan reassured her. "Matt can afford anything you want." She turned to Joyce. "We'll take that one," she told her. "And we'll want coordinating shoes and a bag, as well as at least three other daytime outfits." Kara blinked and held back another protest. If Matt wanted to spend a fortune decking her out as a politician's wife, why should she object? she asked herself resignedly. In a few moments another model appeared, this time in a silk dress with a soft print of lavender and mauve flowers.

"Oh Kara, that's perfect for you," Mrs. Jordan enthused. "We'll take it."

The morning went quickly as Mrs. Jordan helped select what Kara thought was a complete wardrobe, with outfits for everything from tennis to evening dresses for a night at the opera. There were even sheer, sexy nightgowns that Kara was too embarrassed to protest she didn't need.

When Kara, exhausted by what was becoming for her an ordeal, finally glanced at her watch, she found it was almost lunch time.

Mrs. Jordan looked at her daughter-in-law sympathetically. "Shopping can be so tiring," she remarked. "We'll just have your measurements taken and arrange to have the altered garments sent to your house. Then we can have a light lunch."

After this business had been taken care of, Kara waited while her mother-in-law had a last word with Joyce. Then she followed the older woman up the escalator to the terrace level restaurant overlooking the main shopping promenade. They lunched on seafood salad and watched the bustling activity in the mall. Kara was grateful for a place to sit quietly. I'm glad *that's* over, she thought, taking a sip of iced tea. The new clothes were beautiful, but she felt a little as though she were being wrapped up in gold foil and delivered to Matt like a Christmas toy.

The idea amused her, almost making her laugh out loud. Smiling, she said to her mother-in-law, "I can't thank you enough for your help. I've never had so many stunning new outfits all at once in my life."

"But, my dear," Mrs. Jordan exclaimed in surprise. "We're only half finished. We can't leave without finding out what Bloomingdale's has to offer."

"Oh, no . . . of course not," Kara mumbled.

At the end of the meal, a messenger appeared from Joyce's salon with several boxes. Kara looked up in surprise.

"It's that first outfit we saw," Mrs. Jordan explained. "I asked them to hurry with it so you'd have something to wear this evening."

The afternoon was a repeat of the morning, with Kara adding a dozen more outfits to her political wife's wardrobe. By the end of this second shopping session she was truly exhausted and felt the beginnings of an unaccustomed headache.

"I'm afraid I've really worn you out," Mrs. Jordan remarked solicitously, noticing the slump to Kara's shoulders. "Why don't you step into the powder room, change into your new outfit, and fix your makeup. It's almost time to meet Matt."

The saleswoman showed Kara to a gilt and marble dressing area and lavatory where the young woman unfolded the blue linen suit from its box. Then she quickly changed her clothes, fixed her lipstick and eye shadow, and ran a comb through her dark curls.

Changing her outfit and renewing her makeup helped to lift her spirits. Despite her earlier cynicism, she had to admit she was pleased by her new image. "Matt won't have any reason to criticize my clothes now," she said aloud, eyeing her reflection with satisfaction. "That is, until he gets the bills," she added impishly.

With a lightened step she went out to rejoin Mrs. Jordan, but stopped short when she saw Matt, dressed in a dark blue blazer and gray slacks, lounging against the white plaster arch that led into the salon.

He looked at her with approval, his smoky eyes making a detailed survey of her changed appearance.

"Very nice, very nice indeed," he drawled. "And did you also buy something sexy?" he added suggestively. A vivid image of Matt looking at her, clad only in one of the low-cut, sheer nightgowns Mrs.

Jordan had insisted she buy, flashed through her mind, bringing a flush to her cheeks.

"I take that to mean the answer is yes," he teased, observing her heightened color.

"There's nothing sexy that you're likely to see," she shot back, trying to keep the quiver from her voice.

"We'll see about that," he challenged dryly.

Ignoring Matt's taunts, Kara walked back into the salon. Mrs. Jordan was just finishing a conversation with the saleswoman, but she turned to greet Kara and then Matt as he too entered the room.

"We've just finished up," she told her son. "And it has been a long day. I know you said something about having dinner with the two of you, but all I really want to do is go home, prop my feet up and have a hot cup of spiced tea."

"Are you sure?" Matt asked solicitously.

Mrs. Jordan nodded. "Stop trying to pressure me, Matt. You young people need some time alone. You don't require your mother as a chaperone."

Matt chuckled, shooting a surreptitious look at Kara through half-closed eyes. "All right, you've convinced me. But maybe my wife doesn't agree with you."

Kara wanted to protest, but thought better of it. Anything she said under the circumstances would be wrong.

After Mrs. Jordan had kissed them both goodbye, Matt led Kara quickly through Bloomingdale's toward another section of the mall. "There's this terrific little Mexican restaurant I want to take you to," he explained, reaching for her hand and squeezing it. Kara couldn't keep herself from smiling back at him.

Just then they passed in front of a cloth-covered table piled with stacks of political literature. Two well dressed, middle-aged women sat behind the table answering questions for a group of interested bystanders.

"We don't care which party you belong to," one of the women was saying. "But we do want you to consider consumer protection when you vote in the upcoming primary. Would you like a list of the candidates' voting records on consumer issues?"

Kara recognized the speaker. It was Alice O'Neal, an officer in a local women's political action group whom Kara had consulted several times over the toy safety bill.

She put a detaining hand on her husband's arm. "Wait a minute, Matt," she urged. "I want to say hello to these people."

Just then Alice looked up, her eyes warm with recognition. "Why, Kara," she exclaimed. "Congratulations. I heard about your wedding on television."

Kara blushed. "Thank you," she replied. Then an idea struck her. Suddenly she remembered a position paper of Matt's on consumer safety that had crossed her desk. "I'd like you to meet my husband, Matthew Jordan," she said, feeling a surge of pride as she drew the tall, handsome politician toward the table.

Matt gave the women his most charming smile.

"I'm so glad to meet you," Alice bubbled, her eyes wide with admiration.

"Are you familiar with Matt's stand on consumer protection?" Kara asked.

"I know something about it, but I'd really like to have more current literature," Alice replied.

Matt opened his mouth to answer, but Kara rushed ahead. "His support for consumer protection is very strong. You might even want to include his position paper with your handouts."

Matt shot her an amused and curious glance. He was obviously surprised to find her so knowledge-able about his political thinking.

In the next instant he had turned to Alice. "My campaign manager will send you the brochure to-morrow," he promised smoothly. "Actually consumer protection is an issue I'm very interested in. I'd be glad to speak to your group about it sometime soon."

"Well," the woman ventured boldly, glancing at her watch, "we happen to be having a short program here this afternoon. It begins in fifteen minutes. I realize this is awfully short notice, but would you be willing to join the other speakers?"

To Kara's dismay, Matt smiled broadly and accepted without hesitation. She felt a wave of fatigue sweep over her. Attending a long meeting was the last thing she felt like doing now. Maybe she shouldn't have been so quick with her political assistance. She felt a dart of irritation toward Matt. He hadn't even consulted her before accepting the impromptu invitation. But she plastered a politician's wife's smile on her face as she hurried to catch up with Matt, who was already being led toward a cordoned off area at the end of the Mall. There, waiting on the platform, were candidates running for various offices in next month's primary. But, once the program started, Matt's stark good looks and charismatic assurance quickly won the largely female audience's favor.

Kicking off her shoes, Kara took a seat in the back. Although she was tired, Matt's hastily marshaled speech held her attention. She had to admire the way he pulled together his arguments and spun them out in polished sentences.

During the question-and-answer period, he fielded a variety of queries with knowing expertise. He seemed to relish the give and take with the crowd.

The program lasted well over an hour. When the crowd finally began to break up, Kara hastily pulled on her shoes and stood up. In the row in front of her, two women reached for their jackets. One, a short blonde, leaned over and confided to her companion, "I really liked that Matt Jordan. If he were in my district, he'd have my vote and anything else he wanted." Her friend giggled in agreement.

It was a full twenty minutes later before Matt had extricated himself from a group of potential voters and autograph seekers and begun to look around for Kara.

"Oh, there you are," he said at last. "Why didn't you sit in front where you could be seen? I would have introduced you to the crowd."

His criticism sparked her annoyance. "This isn't even your district," she reminded her husband. "Why do you have to be so obliging here?"

"People from my district—like my mother—come shopping here. Besides, it's important to cultivate support all over the state. I thought you realized that when you brought up the consumer safety issue. But

I guess you've got a lot to learn about how politics works."

"I thought I was helping you make a contact, not trading my dinner for a political rally," Kara snapped petulantly. But Matt ignored the challenge in her voice.

By this time they were in the covered parking garage. Matt steered her toward the Porsche. Then he opened the door and helped her in. When he had lowered himself into the plush bucket seat on the driver's side, he turned to Kara.

"A politician has a certain responsibility to the people," he told her. "And I take that responsibility seriously. It means I not only have to look out for their best interests in the legislature, but I also have to be accessible. But that doesn't mean I can't have a private life, too. I've just learned to make the most of every minute when I'm not in the public eye. So let's stop wasting time. We're going to put this incident behind us and have a pleasant dinner together." And then his face broke into a sardonic grin. "Even if it kills us."

Kara couldn't help responding to the absurdity of his last statement. And she grinned back. "Is the food at your Mexican hideout that spicy?" she asked teasingly.

"You'll soon find out," he replied as he began to back out of the parking space.

The restaurant was only a few miles down the road, in an old house set well back from a busy highway. Entering through the enclosed front porch, they were greeted in the hall by the maître d'.

"My wife and I would like some privacy," Matt

told him. "So could you give us a table in the corner of the back room, Jorge."

"*Sí*, Señor Jordan. Follow me," the man replied, shooting Kara a brief, admiring glance.

Jorge led the way through the living room and dining room to a corner table in what must have been a former back bedroom.

Kara looked around. The restaurant was decorated in red and black, with hanging wrought iron lamps and bullfighter posters adorning the walls.

"We'll have Margaritas to start with," Matt told the waiter. Jorge nodded, and they were left alone.

"When do we get the menus," Kara inquired. "I'm starving."

"We don't. The food here is served family style, and you get whatever the chef has fixed for today. But don't worry, it's always delicious, whatever it is."

After Matt and Kara had finished their Margaritas, a waitress came around with a tray of guacamole salads and a side dish of triangular tortilla chips. This was followed by a spicy chicken dish with seasoned rice, cheese enchiladas, soft beef-filled burritos with green chili sauce, and a simple but elegant custard with burnt sugar sauce for dessert.

Kara tried each new dish cautiously. But each was so delicious that she found it hard not to ask for the second helpings she saw some of the other diners requesting.

While they ate they talked.

"It was Lew who introduced me to Mexican food, you know," Matt told Kara. "But the Tex-Mex chili he fed me that first time almost did me in." He smiled at the memory and continued. "I pitched his chili pot in the duck pond, and he pitched me in after it."

The image of a surprised young Matt hitting the water flashed into Kara's mind, and she laughed aloud.

"Well it doesn't seem to have done you any harm," she told him, smiling.

"My mother found out about it, of course. She didn't say anything to me or Lew, but she made the cook spend six weeks learning Mexican dishes. Then she invited me and Lew to a special dinner. And it's a good thing she did too, or I might have thought I hated the stuff."

"And look what you would have missed," Kara told him. "This is all so good, I'd like more of everything. But I've already eaten so much, I'm afraid I won't fit into all those new clothes I got today."

"Tell me about what you bought," Matt questioned, his eyes resting warmly on her face.

"Oh no. I'm not going to," Kara countered playfully. "You'll just have to wait and see as I wear them."

"Well, if you look as good in everything as you do in this outfit, it will be a real treat," Matt assured her.

Kara smiled with pleasure. Matt was being charming. And it was so nice to be able to relax and enjoy his company.

"Would you like an after-dinner liqueur?" he questioned when the waitress had cleared the table.

"Yes," Kara answered, not because she really

wanted the drink, but because she wanted to prolong the pleasure of this dinner together.

"I think amaretto would be just the thing," Matt told her, turning to the waitress. "We'll have two."

As they sipped the sweet, almond-flavored drink from tiny liqueur glasses, Kara felt a warmth steal through her that had nothing to do with the effect of the alcoholic beverage.

Matt leaned across the table and stroked her hand lightly, rubbing the sensitive inside of her wrist with his thumb. Tantalizing sensations began to flicker through her body.

"It's time to go home now," he murmured, looking at his watch and frowning. Not noticing the frown, Kara nodded in agreement, feeling that his words had a special meaning tonight.

In the car on the way home, Matt tuned in some relaxing music. And Kara felt herself becoming drowsy. She settled back in the bucket seat and closed her eyes for just a minute.

"There's something I have to tell you," Matt began. But when he glanced at his bride he stopped in mid-sentence. She was fast asleep.

The next thing Kara knew Matt was shaking her gently. She opened her eyes and looked up. Her head had fallen on his shoulder.

"Come on in the house, sleepy head," he told her gently. But she felt reluctant to move away from the warmth of his strong body and made no effort to straighten up.

"You don't want to sleep out here, do you?" he asked, opening the car door. In a moment he had come around to her side and was helping her out. With an arm across her shoulder, he led her inside.

Automatically she headed up the stairs and down the hall to her bedroom. She had removed the jacket of her new linen suit and was beginning to fumble with the top button on the blouse, when there was a light tap at the door.

Did she want Matt here in her bedroom? she asked herself. The answer was yes.

"Come in," she called softly.

Matt entered, his own jacket off and his tie loosened at the neck of his blue oxford cloth shirt. He looked disturbingly masculine and appealing as he came toward her.

"Kara, I really enjoyed our evening together," he told her.

"I did too," she agreed, feeling a kind of joy she had never allowed herself to experience with Matt before. In a few quick strides, he had crossed the room and pulled her into his arms. This time when his lips took possession of hers, they met no resistance. She felt her body molding itself to his, clamoring for complete union with her husband.

"Matt, oh Matt," she murmured, as his lips brushed her hair.

"Kara, there's something I have to tell you," he responded thickly.

"Darling, whatever it is, it doesn't matter," she whispered, her lips caressing his enticingly as she spoke.

Matt groaned. "Kara you're making this harder for me. But you must listen. Frank Adams has booked me on the eleven P.M. commuter flight to Cumberland. I'm committed to a breakfast speaking engagement at the businessmen's association. I have to leave tonight."

Even though his words were gentle, it was as though he had slapped Kara in the face.

"You mean you're leaving now?" she asked incredulously.

"Yes. My bags are all packed. And Frank will be here to pick me up in a few minutes. The keys to the Porsche and the house will be on the sideboard in the hall."

"Bags?" she asked, stunned.

"It's a week-long campaign trip, Kara. Frank has been telling me how important it is, and I agree."

"But what about us?"

"We'll have to sort that out when I get back. Remember, I tried to explain it to you back in the parking lot. I have my public duties too."

"And they always come first," Kara accused, her violet eyes flashing.

"Not always. But I'm in the middle of a campaign, remember? And these commitments were made before I even knew you existed. Don't make things more difficult for me than they are already. Don't you think I want to stay here with you tonight?"

"I don't know anymore," Kara flung at him.

His eyes hardened as he stared down at her furious face. Without replying he turned on his heels and left her standing in the middle of the room. A few minutes later she heard him descending the stairs. Then the front door slammed, and he was gone.

Like a robot, Kara took off her clothes and got ready for bed. But when her head touched the pillow the reaction from her last emotion-charged scene with Matt enveloped her. She had offered herself to him, and he had spurned her. She felt humiliation and anger at herself.

Why was she leaving herself open to this kind of abuse? She should be cool and able to play the games that Matt wanted without letting him affect her. But she knew that she could never be cool where Matt was concerned. Just being near him aroused a special longing within her—a longing to be loved and to give love in return.

She sat up suddenly as realization dawned on her. Love—that was the key to the whole thing. She was falling in love with Matt Jordan. She knew it now. But this evening just proved the point that *he* didn't love *her*. The kind of intimate, sharing relationship she had always imagined marriage to be could never be possible with a man like Matt.

It can never work, she told herself brokenly as she began to sob at the hopelessness of the situation. It was a long time before the sobs subsided and she fell into a restless sleep.

Chapter Seven

After a night of tossing and turning, Kara awoke feeling even more exhausted. Her disappointment and humiliation at Matt's desertion of her for his campaign trip had made it impossible to sleep.

Kara looked over at the vacant pillow beside her and then laid her hand on it. The cloth was cold to the touch. Would Matt have warmed it if he hadn't gone away? She had a pang of longing for him and remembered back to the night before when she had felt so comforted and protected in his arms. Now she found herself longing to have them around her once more.

Her overwhelming and bittersweet desire shocked her. At first she had feared and despised Matt, but now her heart leapt at the mere thought of him. She really was falling in love with him.

The thought brought her up short. Kara sat up in

bed, shivering again and pulling the covers protectively around her slender body. She thought back, remembering vividly the way Matt had manhandled her in the cabin, the arrogant way he'd snatched her necklace from her throat and later instructed her to clean up the bathroom. And then there were his other women. She was sure he was still seeing them. Why, he'd spent their wedding night with Vera Caldwell and was probably in the redhead's company right now—using his campaign as a convenient excuse. She could not, would not, allow herself to love this infuriating man.

Angrily, she flung back the covers and climbed out of bed. I'm not going to let that womanizer make a fool of me, she told herself briskly.

Kara dressed quickly, pulling on jeans and a flannel shirt. And then she went downstairs and fixed herself a substantial breakfast of scrambled eggs and toast. While she sipped coffee and glanced at the paper, a story about Matt's compaign caught her eye. There was a picture of him talking to a crowd of Howard County farmers. Involuntarily she felt a surge of pride and smiled as she gazed at the image of the handsome, confident-looking man who was now her husband.

Refilling her cup, she put the paper aside and began to walk around the first floor. Entering the spacious living room she made her way across the wood expanse to the sliding glass door and stood looking out at the lake, sparkling like blue silk in the early morning sunshine. Well, Kara, where do you go from here? she asked herself wryly.

She took another sip of coffee and pondered.

Perhaps it was a good thing that Matt had left her alone after all. His absence would give her a chance to think things out. When he was around, his vital personality disarmed her, making it impossible for her to react in the logical fashion on which she prided herself. Should she do what Matt wanted? Should she play the dutiful politician's wife who stood by smiling passively? Or should she show him that she was more than an ornament and take an active role in his campaign? And then there was a third alternative. Should she repack her things and return to her apartment in Georgetown before she got in any deeper? Turning from the window, she wandered idly into Matt's study.

Of all the rooms in his town house, this was the one she liked best. Its warm colors and shelves lined with books made her feel comfortable and even offered her clues to her new husband's personality. Curiously, she explored the shelves, peering at titles on bookjackets. There she found all the political philosophers she would have expected him to know. She ran her fingers over books by Rousseau, Locke, Hobbes, Emerson, Thoreau, Tom Paine and Jefferson. A slim volume, *The Prince,* by Machiavelli, made her turn down her mouth. I should have guessed that despot would be one of his heroes, she told herself.

But the books of poetry on the shelf above surprised her. Collections of John Donne, Keats, Byron and Shelley sat alongside those of Shakespeare, e.e. cummings and Wallace Stevens. Taking out a volume by Donne, she casually flipped it open and was surprised to find the pages were worn.

"Matt must actually read poetry," she murmured in astonishment. The revelation startled her more than almost anything else she had learned about him.

The sound of the phone's shrill ringing jarred her from her musings. "Probably another one of Matt's girlfriends," the young woman muttered as she picked up the receiver.

"Well hello," murmured a familiar male voice. It was Wayne. Kara was taken aback. He was the last person she had expected to hear from in Matt Jordan's house.

"How did you know I was here?" she queried.

"I have my spies," he responded mysteriously. "Actually," he paused, "Jill told me. I've heard about getting married on the rebound, but this is ridiculous, Kara. I can't believe that my levelheaded girl would go out and marry some guy she didn't know just to spite me. You didn't know him, did you? You couldn't possibly love him. You'd make a terrible politician's wife."

Kara held the receiver away from her ear. Wayne's voice droned on in a distant angry buzz. He sounded bitter, like a child whose favorite toy had been taken away. How could I ever have thought I loved that man? she asked herself shuddering. At the moment she felt nothing for him but distaste.

Bringing the receiver to her mouth, she said patiently and with great dignity, "I'm sorry Wayne. It's over. I really don't want to talk to you right now."

"Kara, I've got to see you. I really didn't want to break up. That story about Gloria Ferguson was just a ploy to get you to come around to my way of thinking. We've gotta talk," he insisted.

112

"No, Wayne," Kara said firmly. "It really is over. Good-bye." Very carefully and deliberately she replaced the receiver on its cradle.

The action made her feel more confident. If she could handle Wayne, maybe she could handle other things, as well. Wayne's spiteful words, "You'd make a lousy politician's wife," had smarted. She clenched her fist. Maybe she could show him that was wrong. Ironically, Wayne had unwittingly chosen the path she would take. Perhaps she could work behind the scenes on Matt's campaign. She was, after all, a public relations professional.

"Frank Adams," she said out loud. "That's it, I'll call him and see how I can make myself useful."

After getting the number of Matt's headquarters from information, she dialed the office. Tossing back her hair, Kara asked the volunteer secretary for Matt's campaign manager. While she waited, she tried to pull suggestions together.

"Adams here," a smooth voice replied a moment later.

"This is Kara Barnett, um, I mean Jordan," Kara corrected, catching herself.

"Ah yes, Mrs. Jordan," he said coldly. The distance in his voice made Kara lose some of her resolve. She rubbed the back of her neck nervously and blundered on.

"I was just going to ask, Mr. Adams, if there was some way I could help with Matt's campaign," she ventured.

"In what way?" he questioned sharply.

"Well, I've been a professional public relations person for Citizens for Consumer Protection. I've written press releases and brochures and planned campaign strategies," Kara began to rattle off her credentials. Adams, unimpressed, interrupted her brusquely.

"I've got plenty of public relations people," he said sharply. "I don't need you to throw Matt into impromptu campaign sessions the way you did yesterday at White Flint Mall. As far as I'm concerned that's a waste of his time."

"But Matt thought it was very effective," Kara defended, stung.

"Effective for what?" Adams shot back. "Few of his voters are in that district. In the future, leave those kinds of arrangements to me. That's what Matt pays me for.

"You've done enough for Matt's campaign already," he continued. "The best way you can help is to stay out of trouble, be a good little wife and smile when they take your picture." Kara stared incredulously at the telephone. Hot tears stung the back of her eyes. He sounds like a medieval throwback, she thought irately. Normally his callous manner and brusque dismissal would not have been upsetting. She had learned to handle all types of people in her job. But right now it was just another blow in what was beginning to look like an infinite series.

"I see," she quavered. "Thank you, Mr. Adams."

Hanging up the phone and dropping down into Matt's comfortable desk chair, she stared into space. What now? Kara wondered in frustration. And then she brightened.

"At least I still have my job," she told herself. Sighing, she picked up the phone and dialed the office where both she and Jill had been working for six months. Jill's sunny "Hello" sounded on the other end of the line.

"Oh Jill, it's so good to hear your voice," said Kara with relief.

"Kara, is everything okay?"

"I think so," her former roommate equivocated. "Can we meet for lunch this afternoon? I'm going to stop by the office and pick up the papers on the Toy Safety bill. I intend to come back to work this week. I'll explain when I see you, but I just wanted to let you know I'm okay."

"Are you really married?" Jill questioned with concern.

"I think so. But I hardly believe it myself."

"Well, it really sounds like a whirlwind romance."

"You might say that," Kara responded, smiling despite herself. "I'll see you at one-thirty," she told her nonplussed friend.

That afternoon Kara explained the whole story to the astonished Jill. "But how could you marry him when you still love Wayne?" Jill questioned.

Kara shook her head. "I know now that my feelings toward Wayne were just a mirage. It's over between us."

Jill clamped her hand to her mouth and looked apologetically at her friend. "I'm sorry, Kara. I guess I goofed. When Wayne called me yesterday I told him everything I knew. Fortunately, that wasn't much."

"It's okay, Jill," Kara reassured. "There's not much Wayne can do about it at this point."

After lunch Kara accompanied Jill back to the office, only to encounter another setback. When she

115

asked for her project, her boss told her it had already been assigned to someone else and insisted she go home and take the two-week vacation Matt had arranged for her.

Defeated and angry, she went home and spent the rest of the week shopping and taking several trips out to Windy Willow Farm to help Matt's mother make arrangements for the reception. As Kara and Mrs. Jordan busied themselves with planning and preparations, Kara was drawn more and more to the older woman's warmth and vitality. By the end of the week, Kara found herself sharing little confidences—like the time when she was twelve years old and in a fit of anger had hidden Uncle James' briefcase. She had always been ashamed of the episode, especially since Uncle James, in his frantic search for the missing portfolio, had turned his den upside down while she stood by feigning innocence. Because of her, Uncle James had missed his plane and an important meeting. Now, after all these years she could finally admit her guilt and even laugh about it with this accepting woman.

But despite her newfound closeness with Matt's mother, Kara still hungered for a word from Matt. Evenings, at home in the town house, she waited for a call from her husband. It never came, but she did hear from Matt in another way. One night while half-asleep on the couch in the study, she saw clips from one of his press conferences on the eleven o'clock news. "With only a few weeks left before the primaries," the announcer intoned, "Matt Jordan is making his last bid for votes from farmers in the western part of his district." Pictures of Matt looking handsome and forceful flashed across the screen and Kara noted with irritation that Vera Caldwell was a prominent member of his entourage.

Upset, Kara snapped off the television, marched up to her bedroom and buried herself in a book. The words didn't seem to make any sense though, and she soon gave up trying to follow the plot.

Finally, two days before the reception she got a phone call from Mrs. Jordan.

"I just heard from Matt," the older woman explained. "He'll meet you at the reception, dear."

"Oh," was all Kara could muster. Another wave of rejection swept over her. Why hadn't he called her? She could think of no reason except that he was so busy with Vera Caldwell that he had forgotten his new wife entirely. Well, she would make him remember, she vowed, looking through the phone book for the number of Anton's—an exclusive salon in Columbia. On the afternoon of the party she had an appointment for a manicure, European facial and complete hairstyling.

"Mrs. Jordan, you have the perfect face for a Victorian roll," the hairdresser cooed, arranging her raven tresses in an upswept style that framed her delicate features and made her look romantically sophisticated. Kara nodded approvingly at the lovely image smiling back at her in the mirror. But there was more to come. When Anton had finished with her coiffure, his assistant had moved in with her makeup kit.

"With those fantastic eyes, I think we'll make you into a dreamy turn-of-the-century beauty," the assistant mused as she studied Kara's high cheekbones and large eyes. She set to work, pulling out sponges, brushes and tubes of color. Kara sat entranced watching the woman deftly transform her.

And that evening Kara pulled out the powder blue chiffon designer skirt and blouse. As she touched it she felt excitement bubble up within her. In spite of everything, I'm looking forward to this party and seeing Matt again, she admitted to herself. She felt a pang as she thought of her tall, handsome husband. Why hadn't he called? His neglect puzzled and angered her, but still she had to concede to herself that she was anxious to see him.

After slipping on the layers of blue chiffon and buttoning the matching satin blouse, she stood before the full-length mirror. Then she snapped the pearl-trimmed cummerbund around her waist, slipped on a pair of pearl earrings and stepped back and surveyed her reflection. The woman staring back was beautiful, and Kara turned from side to side, entranced by the effect.

"Oh," she smiled, pleased with herself, "Matt won't be able to ignore me tonight." With lifted spirits, she stepped into a delicate pair of silvery evening sandals and gathered up her silky ecru shawl. Minutes later she was in the Porsche heading toward Windy Willow Farm.

When she pulled into the circular drive, the porti-coed facade of the old stone house stood ablaze with lights. Mrs. Jordan, elegant in a pale rose-colored sheath, greeted Kara with a warm hug. Then the older woman stood back and approvingly surveyed her new daughter-in-law.

"My," she exclaimed with a smile lighting up her aristocratic face, "you will knock eyes out tonight.

They'll just drool over you all evening." Kara beamed, but her face fell when her mother-in-law went on to say, "Matt called. He's not here yet. His plane's been delayed so we'll have to greet the guests without him."

In the ballroom Kara was embraced affectionately by Lew McAlister, who looked uncomfortable in a tuxedo.

"Aren't you the little beauty," he exclaimed, inspecting her with glee. Kara chatted with him for a few minutes before Mrs. Jordan whisked her off to meet some of the other guests.

An hour later Kara found that her mother-in-law's prediction about her success had come true. She had been surrounded by admirers and had found, much to her surprise, it was easy to make conversation with the genteel Maryland society Mrs. Jordan had invited to the reception. Men, especially, hovered around her and many she discovered, to her delight, remembered her mother.

She was the center of a laughing group of admirers when she became conscious of a pair of eyes staring at her from across the spacious room. She looked up. The eyes belonged to Matt. Darkly handsome in expensively tailored evening clothes, her husband was scrutinizing her with an intent expression that she found difficult to interpret. Color flooded her cheeks as her eyes met his and locked. Deliberately setting down his untouched drink on a tray, Matt threaded his way toward her. When he reached her side he bent over and placed a light kiss on her cheek.

"You look beautiful, Kara," he said, his eyes warm with admiration. Then taking her elbow and making apologies to the smiling onlookers, he guided his bride to a quiet corner.

"You seem to be doing very well. The men can't take their eyes off you. And the women who aren't jealous are charmed," he commented wryly.

"Thank you," she said nervously, unsure of how she should respond.

"Well, did you miss me?" he asked, his eyes appraising her with apparent amusement.

"Miss you?" Kara felt a ripple of anger. "That's an odd question to ask, since you didn't even bother to call."

"That was to test you, my dear."

"Test me?"

"I wanted to see if you'd care. Now I have my answer." He grinned with satisfaction, his eyes sweeping over her body with what seemed to Kara a smug possessiveness.

She stiffened. So he had deliberately treated her to an anxious week just to amuse himself. He was toying with her feelings as if she were a mere plaything. Her eyes flashed with anger. She wanted to slap him.

"You, you . . ." she stammered, but before the words formulated, a silky voice interjected itself.

"Matt, dear, I hate to interrupt this charming little domestic scene, but I wanted to ask you about some notes I took in Cumberland," the voice murmured.

Kara turned to see Vera Caldwell, stunningly dressed in an emerald green gown. The redhead was looking coyly up at Matt through her dark mascaraed lashes. "You won't mind if I steal your handsome husband away for a few minutes, will you, dear?" she asked in honey-laden tones.

"Not at all," Kara said through her teeth and watched Vera draw Matt into a vacant corner. They were standing very close together, Kara noted with irritation, Matt's dark head setting off the reporter's glossy lacquered curls. In a minute they were deep into a discussion. Matt seemed to have forgotten his new bride entirely, Kara thought, standing alone and feeling a little piqued.

She looked away, eyes snapping with fury, but at that moment a familiar face caught her eye.

"Wayne," she gasped as the suave, sandy-haired young lawyer made his way toward her.

"What are you doing here?" she exclaimed as he reached her side.

"I came to see you, of course," he replied, favoring her with his most charming smile.

"But, but . . ." she stammered, "I know you weren't invited."

"Come on, Kara. I've lived in Washington long enough to know how to crash a party I've read about on the society pages," he explained with a sly wink. His pale blue eyes swept over her petite form. "Kara, I'd almost forgotten how beautiful you are. I've missed you." But his slurred words told the young woman he had stopped to sample the martini tray before he found her.

Her lips tightened into a thin line. "Wayne, you can't stay here," she whispered urgently. "You've got to leave."

"I'm not going to leave until I've had a chance to talk to you," he insisted loudly. Kara looked around to see if anyone had heard, but conversation continued to drone on around them.

Oh dear, she thought frantically. Somehow she

had to get him out of the house before he made a scene. Searching the room, her eye finally fell on the French doors leading to the garden.

"Wayne, come out on the patio," she urged her would-be suitor.

"Wonderful idea," he agreed readily. "Never did like a room full of stuffed shirts. And I might add, your new husband is the biggest stuffed shirt of all. Just look at him over there playing Mr. Big Shot! He's not going to get my vote. That's for sure!"

Kara held back her retort as she led Wayne through the doors onto the flagstone patio. She had to get rid of him. She drew him off to the side hoping to persuade the slightly tipsy lawyer to get in his car and leave.

But when they were out of sight of the doors, he pulled Kara into a dark corner of the large patio and, seizing her slender arm, began to plead.

"Kara, I want you. This marriage," he argued with a sweeping gesture of dismissal, "is ridiculous. You can't love that pompous politician, and he certainly doesn't love you. Did you see him with that redhead?"

The question scored a direct hit. Kara tried to pull away, but Wayne only became more insistent. "I'm the man you belong with. The thing with Gloria was a mistake. She was never the one for me. You are."

"Wayne," Kara interjected desperately. "Please, I don't want to hear this. It's all over between you and me."

Suddenly anger filled Wayne's pale eyes. "Oh no it's not," he sneered. Forcing her against him roughly, he pressed his lips onto her unwilling mouth.

122

Kara tried to twist herself away but that only made him more persistent.

And then, to her horror, she heard Matt's angry voice.

"What the hell is going on here?" he rasped. Matt's strong hands seized Wayne's shoulders and flung him aside, leaving Kara gasping against the wall. She watched in shock as Matt picked up her ex-boyfriend and tossed him into the bushes.

"Get out of here before I tear you apart," he menaced while Wayne stared at him white-faced from the boxwood.

Hastily the stunned lawyer picked himself up and brushing himself off walked stiffly from the garden, but not before he delivered an angry "All right, I'll leave, but don't write me off yet."

"And as for you," Matt said, turning to the frightened Kara with a furious scowl, "we'll have to settle this after the reception. Now get in there and finish your duty as hostess."

Wordlessly Kara fled from the patio back into the brightly lit reception. Neither she nor Matt had noticed the green-eyed reporter watching with interest from the shadows of a nearby oak tree. As soon as the couple was out of sight, the redhead made her way across the patio and through the hedge where Wayne had disappeared. She smiled when she found the disgruntled lawyer standing near his car.

"I think the two of us have something to discuss," she said silkily.

Chapter Eight

The rest of the evening was a charade. Somehow Kara managed to get through it by pasting an artificial smile on her face and trying not to think of anything beyond the party itself. Though she deliberately avoided looking at Matt, twice during the night her eyes unexpectedly locked with his. The expression of suppressed fury in them made her shiver and quickly glance away.

As the last guest was ushered out the door Kara's apprehension grew. Fruitlessly she tried to think of ways to avoid the confrontation she knew was at hand.

But when Matt appeared at her side, grimly holding out her wrap, she knew that evading him was hopeless. Resigned, she let her husband drape the silky shawl over her slender shoulders. His hands brushed the skin on her arms possessively. Involuntarily she recoiled from his touch, looking up at him in alarm while he observed her through smokey, hooded eyes.

"We're going home now," he ordered, clipping a firm hand around her elbow.

Home, she thought bleakly, what kind of a home was it? More like a jail. But even as she said these words to herself, her jailor was leading her out the door to the silver Porsche.

Inside the sports car the atmosphere was unbearably tense. Kara glanced nervously at Matt. His profile was a set, angry mask, his mouth rigid as he guided the car down the dark ribbon of road.

When she felt she could no longer tolerate the leaden silence, Kara ventured apprehensively, "Matt, let me explain what happened in the garden."

"Save your breath," he ground out, swinging the car sharply around a hairpin curve. The jerky movement of the Porsche pitched her against his shoulder.

"You're driving too fast," she protested, hastily pushing herself away from his body.

"When I want your opinion, I'll ask for it," he returned harshly.

Kara drew in her breath and shut her mouth in an angry snap. The man was an ogre, selfish and uncaring. How could she have ever thought that she had any tender feelings for him or that their marriage might turn into something more than a sham? It's been nothing more than a sparring match, she told herself, and she simply wasn't going to stand for it any longer. She had too much pride to allow him to treat her this way. Maybe his political career was important, but so was her life!

When she remembered the care with which she had dressed for the reception and the eager way she had looked forward to seeing him again, she felt like screaming and breaking the car's ominous silence with bitter words. She clutched her arms around her chest and stared blindly out the window. But her thoughts were interrupted by Matt's tight voice.

"Just get this straight," he warned. "If I ever catch you with that two-bit lawyer friend of yours again, I won't answer for the consequences!" His foot pressed down harder on the accelerator and the car swerved around another turn.

But Kara was too angry to worry about his fast driving. Her eyes smoldered as she glared at him.

"You'll never have that opportunity," she hissed. "I don't plan to stay with you any longer. Too bad about your campaign. I just won't put up with this!"

"You don't have any choice," he grated, shooting her a piercing look from narrowed eyes. "You'll stay married to me as long as I want you to. I don't intend to give you a divorce until I'm good and ready."

So that was how it would be, she told herself, enraged. He intended only to use her and then throw her aside like the other women he had tired of. Well, she would show him!

"I don't need to get a divorce," she challenged, her eyes glittering with triumph. "All I need is an annulment. We've never shared a bed."

The silence in the car stretched painfully, and Kara began to clench her fists nervously as she waited for Matt's reply.

Finally it came. "We'll see about that," his voice said silkily in the darkness. Kara stared at him sharply, wondering exactly what he meant. Then her

126

throat constricted with fear and she felt a sharp pang in the pit of her stomach. With the clarity of sudden insight, she knew this time she had gone too far. Somehow, his soft, suggestive voice in the darkness held more threat than his earlier angry words.

At that moment she was thrown forward as the car jerked to a sudden stop in front of Matt's white stucco town house. Hastily, Kara snapped off the seatbelt, opened the car door and scrambled out. Another wave of alarm swept over her. Quickly she got out her keys and inserted them in the lock of the front door. All her instincts told her she had to get to her bedroom and lock it before he could follow.

But Matt was too quick for her. As she fumbled with the lock, he caught up with her.

"In a hurry to get to bed?" he questioned sensuously. "Well, that makes two of us." His fingers stroked her bare shoulders sending shivers of awareness down her spine. But she would not allow herself to respond.

"Get your hands off me," she whispered hoarsely, pushing him away and making a dash for the stairs. But even as she rushed up the carpeted staircase he was only a step behind. She could feel his breath on her neck. In her haste, the stiletto heels of her sandals twisted underneath her, catching the hem of her long chiffon skirt. As she stumbled, she felt Matt's strong hands on her waist like iron bands.

"Careful now," he cautioned. "The stairs are too uncomfortable for what I have in mind." His firm hand on her elbow restored her balance. Gathering up her skirt, Kara made a headlong rush up the remaining steps and down the hall to her room. She knew that if she didn't get away from Matt now it would be too late. She stumbled through her bedroom doorway and threw herself against the door, but Matt swung it open easily despite her efforts to shut him out. Then he deliberately closed it behind him. The heavy thud it made sent her heart racing.

Her breasts heaving in agitation, Kara took several steps back and confronted her husband. Matt was standing just inside the room, towering over her, his eyes molten with purpose.

"Please leave," Kara whispered. "This is my room!"

"You're mistaken," he countered smoothly. "It's your room only as long as I allow it to be. But now I'm going to claim what's mine—which includes the room and my wife. After tonight, Kara, there aren't going to be any grounds for annulment," he added, his voice soft and suggestive. Loosening his tie, he pulled off his jacket and headed toward her.

Trembling, Kara took another step back. "What —what do you mean?" she stammered.

"You know exactly what I mean," Matt assured her, his voice now gentle and persuasive. With slow, deliberate motions he unbuckled his belt and then began to unbutton his shirt.

Kara stared at him in dawning realization. Her heart began to beat faster and she felt so breathless she wondered if she was going to faint. Matt pulled off the shirt and dropped it on the floor. The sight of his broad, hair-roughened chest was even more disturbing than his voice. Grinning like a cat toying with a mouse, he surveyed her warmly as he removed his shoes and socks.

"It's time for bed, you'd better get undressed," he informed her.

Kara's chin shot out stubbornly. "I will not." She took several more steps backward, but to her chagrin found herself hitting against the edge of the bed.

"I can see that you need some help," he said, a thread of amusement running through his voice as he moved toward her.

"No," she protested. But even to her own ears her voice lacked conviction.

Drawing her close into his embrace with one muscular arm, Matt deftly unsnapped the pearl-encrusted cummerbund. It fell to the floor and in the next moment the chiffon skirt joined it at her feet.

Grasping her waist, Matt pulled her against him. She was acutely conscious of the heat of his body against her naked thighs. Weakly she tried to struggle but she felt her trembling body betray her and mold itself to the masculine contours of his.

She sensed his rapid breathing as he began to unbutton the front of her silk blouse, but she was powerless to stop him. In a moment it was gaping open, revealing her creamy breasts through the sheer lacy wisp of her bra. His half-closed eyes devoured her alluring curves. Her nipples stood out taut against the sheer fabric. Slowly, with provocative deliberation, he bent his head and kissed the deep valley between her jutting breasts, and she felt them swell with desire. The next moment he had unhooked her bra and slipped the blouse from her shoulders.

Sweeping her up, he sat down heavily on the bed, and his eyes began drifting with maddening slowness over her body, examining every part of her as though he were an artist contemplating a portrait. Kara's face reddened at his sensual inspection.

She turned away, too shy to meet his eyes. But cupping her chin in his strong fingers, he forced her to encounter his gaze.

"Kara, you're so beautiful," he murmured against her ear. "There's no reason to be ashamed of showing your body to me. We're married—we're husband and wife."

Like a sculptor memorizing the planes of a beautiful statue with sensitive fingers, Matt traced the fine curves of her body. Her skin burned at his touch. Sensual messages went up and down her nerves like jolts of electric current.

"Matt," she moaned, "I've never slept with anyone before."

He paused, his eyes unfathomable but infinitely kind. "There's nothing to be afraid of, Kara," he reassured softly. "I won't hurt you. I only want to make love to you."

Tenderly he stretched her out on the satin coverlet and gently removed the rest of her clothing and took off his own.

Then Matt began on her hair, methodically pulling out the pins until it lay spread in a lustrous dark fan around her head on the pillow. Musingly, he took a strand of her silky curls and touched it to his lips. She could feel the heavy beating of his heart. Lowering his head, he kissed her lips—this time with fierce passion and a mounting urgency. His voice in her ear was husky.

"Kara, darling, listen to me. . . . There will be no more talk of annulments between us. I'm going to make you mine tonight." His voice deepened possessively, persuasively. "Let me show you how good lovemaking can be between us."

Kara was too overwrought with conflicting emotions to respond coherently. When he began to kiss her—her lips, her temple, the hollow of her throat—she could only moan softly and close her eyes.

His warm hands cupped her breasts and then his fingers circled her nipples until they began to harden with desire. Feeling her response, he lowered his mouth to her breasts. While his lips teased her nipples, his hands stroked the flat surface of her stomach and then drifted down.

Flames began to lick dangerously through Kara's veins. Frightened of the passion stirring within her, she tried to fight the hot desire he was arousing in her, but his exploring lips and prowling fingers fanned the coals of her awakening passion into a raging conflagration. Expertly, he traced a random pattern over the most sensitive areas of her body, making her ache with need for him, arousing feelings she had never known she possessed. At last, caught up in his sensuous warmth, her body arched toward Matt, unconsciously demanding fulfillment.

With a groan, he covered her soft body with his hard one and kissed her deeply. She could hear the ragged effort of his breathing.

"Kara, sweetheart, I can't wait any longer," he whispered urgently. "I'll be as gentle as I can."

With a low moan of urgency, she clasped his head in her hands and held him to her. The center of her being was melting like a wax candle in flame. She ached with undeniable longing.

"Oh please," she murmured.

He swept her up, his strong, rhythmic movements carrying her high on a wave of sensation.

She was lost, drowning in feelings beyond description. She and Matt were fused together in white heat and she cried out in ecstasy as he arched above her.

"Oh, Kara," he whispered, his voice drugged with pleasure as he clasped her to him. "I've wanted you so much. . . . It's all I've been thinking of this week. And now you're mine. I've never wanted any woman as much as I've wanted you."

His lips descended on hers tenderly. All her earlier anger and fear had been washed away by the fulfillment of his lovemaking.

"Oh, Matt," she sighed, trying to move closer to the warmth of his body. There was no question in her mind now that she loved her husband. She admitted that now. She had wanted him to make love to her—had wanted it from the moment he first kissed her in Uncle James' cabin.

They held each other close until Kara shivered, aware for the first time of the cold night air on her unprotected body. Sensing her discomfort, Matt lifted her tenderly in his arms and swept back the covers.

"Time to get under the sheets, Mrs. Jordan," he murmured in her ear as he settled the blankets around both of them. He wrapped her in the warmth of his arms and they held each other till morning.

Chapter Nine

Kara snuggled deeper into the covers, seeking the warmth of Matt's body that had been curled so protectively around hers during the night. But although his side of the bed was still warm, he was no longer there.

She felt a little stab of disappointment not having him beside her when she awoke. But he had probably gotten up to prepare breakfast. After all, this would be their real wedding morning together. She smiled, remembering the joy Matt had brought her the night before. It had been wonderful. She had never dreamed that lovemaking could be such a wondrous experience.

She knew now that she and Matt were made for each other. All the doubts that had plagued her before had been swept away by the sweet fulfillment of their lovemaking. It was true Matt hadn't yet said that he loved her—but then neither had she confessed her feelings for him. Words had seemed unnecessary at the time. But now, in the rosy morning afterglow of their shared intimacy, Kara felt a compelling need to tell Matt how she felt.

After pulling on her robe and slippers, Kara ran a comb through her tousled curls. Curiously she inspected her face in the mirror. She could see that her violet eyes had a new sparkle and her complexion seemed to glow. The fulfillment of her love for Matt last night had actually transformed her outward appearance, she noted with a shy smile.

With a light step, Kara headed for the kitchen. But halfway down the stairs, she heard Matt talking to someone in the living room and stopped in her tracks.

"I'm glad you came by," he was saying.

"Well, I wanted to make sure that you convinced that surprise wife of yours to fulfill her part of the bargain," the voice of Frank Adams responded.

"Oh, she's convinced," Matt chuckled. "She's being very cooperative."

Kara gasped and pressed her hand to her mouth as the realization of what Matt was saying hit her in the face like a slap.

"Well, from the way you two were acting when you left the party last night, I was afraid she wouldn't come with you to the Preakness today. And you know how important it is for you to be seen there together," the campaign manager was saying.

Face burning, Kara held her breath, waiting to hear what her husband would say.

"I know how to get along with Kara," Matt

134

assured Adams. "So you just worry about the more conventional campaign details."

The other man snickered. "I've always envied your ability to handle women," he drawled suggestively.

The two men walked into the hall, and Kara, her fury rising, pressed herself back around the corner of the stairs so she would not be seen. After she heard the front door open and close, she marched down into the hall and stood glaring at Matt.

"So now I know what last night meant to you," she flung at him. "You don't care about me at all—I'm just a troublesome cog in your well oiled campaign machine."

Matt's face was an expressionless mask. "I'm sorry you heard that conversation, but it doesn't mean what you think it does," he said harshly, all traces of his previous good humor wiped from his voice. There was a waiting, intense look in his gray eyes. But Kara plunged ahead.

"I'm surprised you didn't reassure Frank Adams that there weren't grounds for an annulment," she shot back sarcastically. "Or did I miss that part of the conversation?"

"I don't know how much of the conversation you missed," Matt said, his voice steady and controlled. "How long were you eavesdropping this time? You're becoming such an expert that I never know when you're hearing part of a discussion out of context." Without waiting for an answer, he stalked past Kara and headed through the living room toward the kitchen.

Impotent with rage, she followed.

Matt stood by the sink, filling the coffee pot with

water. "I don't know about you, but I'd like something to eat before we leave for the Preakness."

"If you think that I'm going to that horse race with you, you're a more conceited, self-centered politician than I ever dreamed possible. You didn't even do me the courtesy of telling me we were going," Kara accused, standing stiffly near the kitchen door.

"You might as well sit down and make yourself comfortable," Matt told her, gesturing toward one of the kitchen chairs. "If you didn't know that the Preakness was today, then blame your uncle. I've been away all week, remember, and he was supposed to call and tell you about it. We're meeting him there, as a matter of fact."

Kara maintained a resentful silence. She made no move to pull out a chair.

Matt turned around and looked her squarely in the face. "I don't understand you at all," he said in exasperation. "One minute you respond like a woman and the next minute you're throwing a childish temper tantrum. What's the matter with you, anyway?"

"The matter with me?" Kara sputtered. "It's you who . . ."

But the dangerous look in his eyes made her stop her accusation in mid-sentence.

"I've had all of this I'm going to take today," Matt declared, enunciating every word carefully. "You're going to have some breakfast. Then you're going to go upstairs and get dressed in one of your new dresses. And then we're going to go to the Preakness together. Do you understand?" he commanded autocratically.

Kara nodded miserably, not trusting herself to

speak. She knew now she understood Matt Jordan perfectly. He was out to take what he could get, from her and everyone else. And she was a fool to be in love with him. As soon as the campaign was over, she was going to end this charade and force herself to forget about him. But there was no escape for the moment. She would go with him to the Preakness. She would do what was required in public. But in private she would put her emotions on ice. She would build a cool wall of reserve around herself, a wall that Matt Jordan would not break through again.

Breakfast was a silent meal. And afterwards Kara went upstairs and took her time making her toilet and putting on a yellow cotton sundress with a matching jacket. White leather sandals and a small white purse completed the outfit. When she came downstairs again, Matt was sitting in the living room wearing a stylish but casual sport shirt and slacks.

Determinedly Kara forced herself to ignore his sensual attractiveness and look away. She would not let herself think about the feel of his muscular torso or the way he had pulled her to him and held her so tenderly the night before.

She and Matt did not speak to each other during the first part of the drive on the Baltimore Beltway toward Pimlico Race Track. But as they approached the congested area near the entrance, Matt began explaining about the race in the neutral voice of a tour guide.

"This is the one-hundred-seventh annual running of the Preakness. It's the second jewel of racing's triple crown—after the Kentucky Derby and before the Belmont Stakes," he offered.

Kara nodded.

"Have you ever been here before?" he asked casually as he pulled into the special parking lot reserved for VIPs.

Kara shook her head.

Matt turned to her with a quizzical expression. "Surely you're not going to be so childish as to give me the silent treatment all afternoon?" he queried.

"Certainly not," she snapped.

"That's better—I think," he replied mockingly.

She held herself stiffly as he helped her out of the car and led her up the concrete ramp to the track's main gate.

Kara looked up in surprise. Spread out before her in the spacious infield was what looked like a country fair.

At either end of the wide oval track were two bands—one playing popular rock selections and the other belting out country and bluegrass tunes. In between were blue-and-white-striped booths selling all kinds of food—roasted corn, crabs, fried dough, hamburgers, barbecued sandwiches and pit beef. Others featured various drinks—everything from colas and beer to black-eyed Susans, a mixed drink named after the Maryland state flower.

She could see thousands of spectators, making themselves at home for a day of partying at the races. Many had blankets spread on the grass. Some had brought their own picnic lunches and kegs of beer.

Part of the field had been roped off for lacrosse games. As they walked by they stopped for a minute to watch the teams tossing the small, hard ball back and forth with their sticks.

"When they show the Preakness on TV, you never see all this," Kara exclaimed, caught up in the excitement of the event in spite of herself.

"This is Baltimore's biggest party. By the time the day is over, there will have been eighty-five thousand people here," Matt replied, warming to the festive atmosphere.

"It doesn't seem that crowded," Kara commented.

"That's because the infield is so big. Actually this is the only day of the season they open it like this. Usually people sit in the grandstands, and we'll be going up there later to watch the Preakness. But there's a full bill of racing before the big event."

Despite her resolution of the morning, Kara couldn't help enjoying the lively goings-on. And why shouldn't I have a good time? she asked herself. I might as well get something positive out of being Mrs. Matt Jordan, she justified to herself.

She and Matt spent the morning strolling among the merrymakers. As they approached various groups, many in the crowd recognized Matt and greeted him warmly. But few were interested in a sober discussion of political issues.

"You don't seem like you're doing much campaigning," Kara teased.

Matt laughed good humoredly. "It's important for us to be seen here, Kara—you should understand that, since you recommended that I relate to the public—but most of those here are more interested in having a good time than getting involved in serious discussions."

Matt and Kara lunched on crab cakes, corn on the cob and beer. After they ate, he handed her a program. "It's a lot more fun if you place a bet on the Preakness," he explained.

"How do I pick the winner?" she asked, smiling mischievously up at him.

Matt chuckled. "If I could tell you how to do that, I'd be a billionaire. Just use your intuition. Then we can go stand in line at the betting booth."

Kara looked over the list of eleven horses. There was only one filly—Fool's Delight. The jockey would be wearing the buff and blue silks of a Kentucky stable. She decided to bet on the filly.

"You picked a fifty-to-one shot," Matt informed her. "If she does win, you'll be set up for life."

Kara giggled. "Maybe I'll have beginner's luck."

"Well, I'm going to bet on my mother's foal—Maryland Dancer—who has only slightly better odds," Matt replied. "Let's go over to the window now. It's a good idea to place your Preakness bet early. By the middle of the afternoon, the line will be half a mile long."

After they had placed their bets, they heard the loudspeaker announce the first race. Kara was surprised to see all the merrymakers drop what they were doing and rush to the railing to watch the horses run. Two minutes later, when the results were announced, they all resumed their activities on the infield as if there had never been an interruption.

Kara turned to Matt quizzically. "What was all that?" she asked.

"Just the attendees taking a small intermission for the race. Actually, the preliminary races are only a minor part of what Preakness day is all about."

"Are all horse races like this?" she asked.

"Hardly. Most of the people here today are

once-a-year racing fans. They're mostly interested in the celebration and having a good time, and the races are just an added bonus."

As they walked along the field, Kara almost tripped over a couple who had shed much of their clothing and were sunbathing on a blanket on the grass.

"This certainly is informal," she observed, averting her eyes in embarrassment. She felt herself flushing as she recalled vividly how Matt had disrobed her the night before.

"You should have been here a few years ago when streaking was popular," he replied easily, not seeming to notice her discomfiture.

The afternoon flew by. And before Kara knew it, the Preakness was being announced.

"We'd better get up to the grandstands," Matt told her, taking her elbow and walking her quickly across the field. "They'll close off this section once they start raking the track, and we don't want to be stuck over here."

In the grandstands, Kara and Matt found their seats in the booth that had been reserved for party officials.

"Where's Uncle James?" Kara questioned. "I don't see him anywhere."

"Your guess is as good as mine," Matt replied laconically.

"Are you sure he's really supposed to meet us here?" Kara persisted. "Or did you just tell me that to get me here?" she added suspiciously.

Matt shot her a look of annoyance. "Are you questioning my integrity?" he asked in a low voice, trying to keep the argument private.

Kara gave a mirthless laugh. "Integrity," she retorted. "For someone who admitted to using me for his own purposes, you're a fine one to talk about integrity."

"You may be taking advantage of your uncle's absence as an excuse to start an argument, but I'm not playing your game," Matt informed her. "If you're not going to watch the race, at least let me see who wins."

Kara looked at Matt questioningly. How could he concentrate on something as unimportant as a horse race with so much strain between them?

Suddenly all the emotions he had aroused in her this morning came flooding back. It was all she could do to force herself to stay seated next to him.

She had played into his hands again today, she realized. Matt had made no secret of the fact that he wanted her to be two things as a wife—a showy political possession and a willing bedpartner. Well, in the last twenty-four hours he had certainly gotten what he wanted, she told herself grimly.

She was only vaguely aware of the horse race, as the people around her sprang from their seats for a better view. But her own thoughts about the hopelessness of her marriage kept her from getting caught up in the excitement.

It was only after the eleven horses had finished and she heard the announcer give the final standings that the voice from the loudspeaker was able to penetrate her haze.

Her horse, Fool's Delight, had come in last.

How appropriate, Kara thought. I should have known that fools never win. She tore the ticket she was clutching into a dozen pieces.

"We might as well leave," she heard Matt saying. And obediently she stood up. But just as they reached the aisle, a short, bald man in a brown suit came rushing up to Matt.

"Mr. Jordan?" he asked breathlessly.

Matt nodded.

"I have an important message for you," he said, handing him a folded slip of paper.

Matt thanked him and opened the note. His eyes scanned the words quickly and a dark frown spread across his features. Then he turned to Kara.

"It's your uncle," he said gently, putting his arm around her shoulder. "He's had a heart attack. We've got to get to the hospital right away."

Chapter Ten

Kara sat frozen in shock in the Porsche's front seat while Matt threaded his way through Preakness traffic toward Johns Hopkins Hospital. The car crawled at a snail's pace. Every block seemed to take an hour to traverse. Crowds of festive people lined the streets, and open automobile windows invited joking back and forth. But what had seemed fun and exciting during the Preakness festival was now nightmarish and grotesque to Kara.

She couldn't believe that her uncle was critically ill. She tried to picture him lying helpless in a hospital bed, but the image wouldn't materialize. He had always seemed so strong and unassailable.

"I can't believe this is real," Kara said aloud. Matt, somber behind the wheel, turned and looked at her sympathetically.

"But it is. Your uncle has been sick for a long time, Kara," he said softly.

She stared at him in shock. "What do you mean?"

"He's had a severe heart condition for seven years and he's had to be very careful," Matt explained. "These last two years have been especially rough for him because his condition has grown worse."

"I had no idea," Kara gasped, tears beginning to well up. "Oh poor Uncle James!" Matt pulled a handkerchief out of his pocket and handed it to her. She dabbed at her eyes and then looked up at his firm profile.

"But how did you find out about all of this," she asked, "when I had no idea he was even ill?"

"I only learned about it on our wedding night. Monica called to ask for my help. James had had a mild attack and fallen on the floor. She couldn't get him into bed and he refused to allow her to call the hospital."

Before she could stop herself she blurted, "Isn't it a good thing he always has a girlfriend around recently."

Matt picked up her meaning immediately. "It is a good thing, Kara, despite what you're thinking. But there was nothing accidental about it. Monica is a special duty nurse just like the other women he's been seen with. He's been hiring them to take care of him since his condition worsened two years ago."

Kara flushed with chagrin. "I'm sorry. I had no idea," she murmured contritely, staring down at her folded hands. "I always thought those girls were . . ."

"I know what you thought," Matt interrupted. "I

did, too, before Monica's phone call, but that was what your uncle wanted people to think. He was too proud to let anyone know he was seriously ill, even you."

Kara sank into the seat and stared miserably out the window. They had finally gotten through the worst of Preakness traffic and were heading down Northern Parkway to Cathedral. A half hour later they pulled up in front of the red brick Victorian facade of one of Baltimore's largest medical complexes.

"Why don't you go in and check on your uncle while I park the car," Matt suggested. "I'll meet you up there." She nodded, pulled open the door and climbed out.

She walked into the hospital with a sense of unreality. There was a queasy feeling in the pit of her stomach. It all seemed like a bad dream from which she would soon awaken. Passing a hand quickly over her eyes, she squared her shoulders and went to the main desk, where she inquired about her uncle.

The receptionist checked a register. "Mr. Barnett's still in intensive care. But the ICU will have more information on his condition. Take the elevator through those doors to the fourth floor and look for the signs."

Following the woman's instructions, Kara soon found herself in a brightly lit corridor on the fourth floor. Nurses and hospital staff in white uniforms floated by her. An antiseptic smell greeted her nostrils, and as she walked her high heels tapped eerily on the tile floor. The hall seemed unending as she passed doorway after doorway. But finally she reached the intensive care unit. There a nurse in a small reception area stopped her.

"I'm here to see my uncle, James Barnett," Kara said in a shaky voice. "I'm Kara Barnett."

The nurse looked down at a sheet of paper. "The only people who have permission to see Mr. Barnett," she told Kara officiously, "are a Mr. and Mrs. Matthew Jordan."

"Oh, I'm Mrs. Jordan; Barnett is my maiden name," Kara explained in embarrassment. The nurse looked at her doubtfully and then asked her to wait.

A few minutes later a tall, freckled man in a white coat came out and introduced himself as Dr. Shepherd. He reached in a friendly fashion to take Kara's cold hand, wrapping his big, warm mitts around hers.

"Your uncle has been asking for you," he told her sympathetically. "You can go in and take a peek at him. But don't disturb him. He's sleeping now and he's not strong enough to carry on a conversation. You should be able to talk to him in a day or two." He opened the door and let her through, warning, "Remember, only a minute now."

Kara thanked him and stepped inside. She stopped short. What she saw confused her at first. Machinery cluttered the room. Even the bed in the center was not spared. A large plastic tent covered her uncle's sleeping form and lines from an IV unit were attached to his arm. She moved closer while a nurse hovered at his side.

When Kara peered down through the plastic she was shocked at her uncle's haggard, gray appearance. She hardly recognized him. The man in the oxygen tent seemed at least twenty years older. She could feel the tears well up once again. He was her only blood relative and now it looked as if she might lose him. Why had she done so little to communicate with him over the past few years? she wondered remorsefully.

Suddenly Matt was at her side, holding her hand. "We'd better go now," he told her gently. Putting an arm around her, he led her out into the waiting room. Distractedly she listened to him talking to Dr. Shepherd, asking him to keep them informed.

The rest of the evening passed in a haze for Kara. Torn by conflicting emotions of fear, guilt, and loss, she went immediately to her room after Matt took them home.

Later in the evening Matt tapped on her door and asked, "Kara, are you okay?"

"Yes, I am." she said through the closed door. "But I'd like to be alone tonight, Matt."

"Can't I get you something to eat?" he persisted.

"No thanks. I just need some sleep." He paused for a moment and then said "All right" in a low voice. Then she heard his footsteps crossing the hall.

The next three days Kara spent sitting by her uncle's side or in the small, impersonal waiting room at the hospital. Matt was busy during the day, but he joined her in the evening and led her down to the cafeteria to eat. Food had no taste, but she dutifully forced herself to eat a little at Matt's urging.

On Tuesday, when Matt came to take Kara home from the hospital, he frowned at her pale face and lackluster eyes.

"Stop punishing yourself," he told her sternly. "None of this is your fault."

Kara's eyes fell away from his. "I know you're right," she murmured. "But it's so hard to be rational at a time like this. I'm doing more feeling than thinking. All those years Uncle James did the best he could for me. I thought he was insensitive. . . ." She let her voice trail off.

Matt put a strong arm around her shoulder and drew her to his side. Too weary to resist, she let herself rest her head against the muscular wall of his chest. At this moment he seemed like a rock she could cling to in the storm of emotions she was feeling.

"You need a change of scene and a good meal. Let's go down to the Inner Harbor," he suggested.

"Oh, I'm not in the mood for anything like that," Kara started to protest. But Matt would not take no for an answer. Before she knew it she found herself settled in the bucket seat of his Porsche as he threaded his way through traffic toward Baltimore's newly restored waterfront.

In less than fifteen minutes the striking glass and steel pavilions of Harborplace swung into view. And as Kara caught a glimpse of the street corner musicians and crowds of strollers taking in the harbor's red brick promenades, she felt her mood lighten. They joined the throngs of sightseers, stopping to admire the tall masts of the sailboats moored at the finger piers.

As Kara breathed in, she was astonished to catch the spicy scent of warm cinnamon on the light breeze ruffling the flags of the sailboats. "What's that delicious aroma?" she asked in surprise.

Matt grinned. "One of Baltimore's chief delights," he supplied, gesturing toward the creamy stucco building across the road. "The McCormick Spice Company is obviously grinding cinnamon today."

Delighted, Kara laughed for the first time in days as she took in another heady whiff of the marvelous scent. Matt smiled warmly down at her, squeezing her shoulder gently before he began to lead her toward the Light Street Pavilion, where he had made reservations at an Italian restaurant.

A few minutes later a maître d' seated Kara and Matt next to a floor-to-ceiling window overlooking the harbor. The elegant dining room had a striking decor of white tile accented with touches of black and chrome. On each table there was a red carnation in a cut glass bud vase. Kara looked around appreciatively and then smiled shyly. Matt was right; she had been too caught up in her uncle's illness. This break was just what she needed, and she felt grateful to Matt for his thoughtfulness in suggesting it. But when she told him so, he only smiled and then changed the subject to food.

After they had ordered, they began talking about his campaign; she realized with a start that the primary was only a week away.

"How did you ever find the time to get away like this?" she questioned, realizing how hectic his schedule must be. He took her hand and squeezed it. "I'm learning how to make time for things that are really important," he told her with a meaningful smile. But before she could react, the waiter appeared with their dinners.

While they ate and sipped their wine, they watched the sunset. By the time they had finished their coffee, it was night and the harbor's lights were sending out glittering reflections over the rippled surface of the dark water.

When they left the restaurant, Matt took her hand and continued to hold it while they strolled once more along the promenade. On a whimsical impulse he stopped to buy her a shiny, heart-shaped balloon, giving it to her with a wry grin and laughing as she let it bob along behind her shoulder while they made their way back to the parking lot.

She was in a mellow mood as they pulled up to the white stucco town house, and so was Matt. The moment the front door was closed behind them, he took her in his arms.

"I've missed you," he whispered, his breath warm in her ear. And then, very carefully, he released the balloon's string from her fingers and let it float slowly to the ceiling.

As Matt's warm lips descended on hers, Kara too felt that she was floating. His lips slid from her mouth to her neck, tracking a path of fire along her throat as his hands massaged the small of her back and then pressed her even closer to the hard contours of his lean body. Earlier that afternoon she had told Matt that she was capable only of feeling, not thinking. And that was certainly true now. All rational thought submerged as she responded to the persuasion of Matt's sensitive caresses and skillful hands. She didn't even realize that he had unbuttoned her silky shirtwaist dress until she felt his warm fingers on her bared midriff. One hand moved possessively around her breast, stroking her nipple through the lacy material of her bra. As if from far away, she heard herself moaning with pleasure as she felt his touch.

He opened her lips to his probing tongue and then whispered in her ear, "We'll be more comfortable in *my* bed this time."

But far from the effect Matt had planned, the words jolted Kara back to reality. Last time, she reminded herself, after she had given herself to Matt, she heard him laughing about her the next morning with his campaign manager. Their love-making had meant nothing to him. He had made a fool of her then, but he wasn't going to do it again.

She stiffened, and Matt, feeling her change of mood, looked down into her set face, frowning. "What's wrong?" he demanded.

Kara looked away, casting around for an excuse to get out of this situation. "I'm sorry Matt. I keep thinking about my uncle, and I'm just not in the mood."

Matt's frown deepened and his arms fell away. She watched as for a moment he visibly struggled with his emotions. When he had pulled himself together, a rueful smile crossed his face.

"All right, I understand. But I think I'd better go take a cold shower," he said with an attempt at lightness. Turning, he moved toward the stairs. But then he paused and looked at Kara over his shoulder. "Care to join me?" he asked hopefully. Kara smiled despite herself and then firmly shook her head.

When Kara awoke the next morning Matt had already left for campaign headquarters. But there was a note on the kitchen table signed with his slanting scrawl. "Meet you at the hospital this afternoon," it said.

152

After a hasty breakfast of toast and coffee, she donned the pale cream designer suit that she and Mrs. Jordan had bought at White Flint. Tying the bow on her delicately flowered blouse, she inspected herself in the mirror.

Even with the fancy designer label in her clothing, she definitely didn't look her best. The tension of the last few days and the worry over Uncle James had taken their toll. But when she arrived at the hospital she found her uncle's condition had improved enough so that he had been transferred to a private room. It was there that she had her first real conversation with him. Though he was still hooked up to IV's and had a special duty nurse, he was now free of the oxygen tent.

Later that morning, as Kara sat next to him, he opened his eyes and looked directly at her.

"Kara," he whispered, smiling and asking her to move closer. "Public relations is the wrong calling for you. You should have been a nurse."

Kara blushed and smiled shyly back at him. "I've been so worried about you," she volunteered.

"I've been worried about me, too," he said good naturedly, "but I'm feeling better now. I think I'm going to make it. But I want you to know that's partly your doing. Having you here like this has made a big difference. You're truly a fine person, and I'm proud of you. I'm sorry I haven't seen more of you."

Kara looked away in acute discomfort. Was he apologizing now for the past?

"I know we weren't close when you were a teen-ager," James went on. "I deeply regret that.

153

When your parents died, I tried to be a substitute, but I had no real experience with children. And then this old heart of mine started to act up, so I didn't try to stop you from moving out."

"Oh, I wish you had told me," Kara exclaimed, "it would have made such a difference if I had known." She smiled at him through wet eyes. He had cared about her. She glowed with the thought. But as she beamed at him, she noticed that he was knitting his brow, looking at her with an expression of concern on his drawn, colorless face.

"Kara, there's something that's been bothering me deeply for the past few weeks. I can't tell you how guilty I feel about that marriage I forced you into," the old man said, squeezing her hand. "You must tell me how you really feel about it. If you're truly unhappy, I'll do all I can to find a way out of it for you."

Kara's eyelashes fluttered nervously, and she looked down at her lap. How did she feel about her marriage now? What were her feelings toward Matt? And more important, what were his feelings toward her? He still found her desirable; she knew that from last night. But he had given her no indication that his feelings went beyond a mere physical attraction. He hadn't said, "I love you," and she despaired that he ever would.

Uncertainty began to well up in her as she reflected on the unnerving twists and turns her life had taken in recent weeks. Yes, she was unhappy. But it was better to keep her turmoil hidden from her Uncle James. He looked too frail right now she decided.

Masking her unhappiness, she gave James a bright smile. "It's okay. Things will work themselves out eventually."

Then, hastily changing the subject, she said, "There's something I've been wanting to ask you. I've never understood your association with Matt. Why does a staunch party-supporter like you align himself with a crusading reformer like Matt?"

Unexpectedly, James grinned sheepishly. "You don't think much of my politics, do you?"

Kara blushed and looked embarrassed. The old man continued. "I had come to the conclusion that my longtime unquestioning support of machine politics was a mistake. I think it's time to clean out the stables, so to speak," he said to her with a rueful smile. "And I think Matt's the man to do it."

A little stab of pride hit her as she heard his words. Yes, maybe Uncle James was right. Maybe Matt was the man to do it. She knew from personal experience, she thought ironically, that when Matt went after something he usually got it.

Just then the nurse came in and announced, "Mr. Barnett needs to rest now." Putting down a tray of medicine, she fluffed up his pillow. "Time for your yellow pills," she singsonged cheerfully. Grinning, Kara took her uncle's hand, squeezed it and then left the room.

As she closed the door she almost bumped into Monica. The slender blonde looked smart and professional in a crisp, white uniform. Kara felt embarrassed when she remembered that she had thought Monica was one of Uncle James' bedmates. How unjust she had been to both of them.

But Monica appeared unconscious of Kara's earlier prejudice, and gave the dark-haired young woman a friendly "How are you?"

"I'm fine now that my uncle is so much improved," Kara returned.

"Yes, I'm relieved too," the nurse agreed. "Now that your uncle's out of the ICU, where they don't allow private duty nurses, I'm back on the case. I feel as if I haven't been away at all. As soon as he sees me he'll probably start complaining about the hospital food and demanding his waterbed."

"His waterbed?" Kara asked in confusion.

"Yes, for his arthritic condition," Monica explained cheerfully, entering the room and leaving Kara in the hall, uncomfortable again at the thought of her assumptions.

As the door closed behind her, Kara rubbed her eyes and suddenly realized how tired she was. Even though her uncle now seemed out of danger, there was no denying that the past few days had been an ordeal, and she felt drained by it.

Heading toward the elevator, she pressed the down button. What she needed was a cup of coffee in the hospital cafeteria before Matt stopped in to see how her uncle was doing.

Quickly she purchased a cup of black coffee and brought it to a small, red formica table. Slumping with fatigue into the hard, plastic chair, she fell into a reverie. Unexpectedly she found herself looking forward to seeing Matt. Perhaps they could work things out yet.

But her daydreams were rudely blown away by the pair of hostile eyes she felt burning the back of her neck. She turned suddenly to see Vera Caldwell sitting at a table directly behind her, chain-smoking. A pile of used cigarettes littered the foil ashtray in front of the reporter, and cigarette smoke wreathed her brilliant red curls. Kara shuddered involuntarily. What was that woman doing staring at her like that?

Crushing out a half-smoked cigarette, Vera pushed back her chair with a scrape and moved toward Kara. Her stiletto heels made sharp, clicking noises on the shiny, tiled floor of the cafeteria.

Without asking, Vera pulled out a chair at the other side of the table and sat down, smoothing out the knife pleats of her black linen skirt. She was outfitted as usual in the height of fashion, and although Kara had dressed carefully that morning, she suddenly felt rumpled and grimy.

"I've been hoping to see you here," the redhead began in clipped tones as she eyed the young woman through long, mascaraed lashes.

"Oh," Kara replied blankly, wondering what the reporter could want with her.

"I'm waiting for an opportunity to interview your uncle, of course," Vera went on. "But I also want to talk to you."

"To me?" Kara questioned. "What about?"

"About Matt, what else?" the reporter retorted, watching Kara intently. Before continuing, Vera slowly lit another cigarette, inhaled and coolly blew out a thin cloud of grayish smoke.

Stifling a cough, Kara demanded, "What can you possibly have to say to me about Matt?"

"I have a great deal to say about him. Matt and I go way back," she said, her eyes narrowing as she looked the younger woman up and down critically. "We've known each other for a long time. We're old and dear friends and I hate to see his life ruined by a foolish marriage. You and I know that Matt was forced into this by your uncle. He would never have chosen to marry a naïve little piece of baggage under other circumstances."

Kara gasped. She felt Vera's words pierce her heart. The reporter had said exactly what Kara had feared herself. How could someone as young and unsophisticated as herself ever hope to earn the love and respect of a polished man of the world like Matt? It was true, she thought, hating Vera for having said it out loud. Kara tried to lift the coffee cup to her lips but her fingers were shaking, so she quickly set it back on the table.

Vera's green eyes watched Kara's trembling hands with satisfaction. "You know what I'm saying is the truth," she pressed her advantage. "You're not the right woman for Matt and you never will be. At best, he'll only tolerate you and seek consolation in the arms of another woman," Vera added with a knowing smile.

Kara felt another twinge of pain. She feared that Matt had already done that. In fact, she wondered if the sleek journalist before her was the woman. She remembered the image of Matt's dark head next to the reporter's red curls at the reception. And then there were those television news broadcasts showing Matt and Vera deep in discussions on Maryland politics. What had they discussed, she wondered, when they were not on film? Or had they wasted time on words at all?

Vera's voice interrupted her thoughts. "I don't know what your plans are, but I recommend you divorce Matt immediately after the election. I know that's what he wants."

"How could you possibly know?" Kara parried, mustering every bit of courage she could.

"Because," said the reporter smiling triumphantly at her victim, "Matt told me so." Kara stiffened while Vera twisted the knife a little deeper. "Matt has told me that your marriage is nothing more than a joke and that he wishes he'd never set eyes on your uncle's cabin. He feels trapped," she said with a haughty air, "but I intend to set him free. If you don't agree to a divorce after the election, I'll make sure the details of your little plot to entrap him are leaked to the press. You and your uncle will be the laughing stocks of the whole state."

"If you write a scandalous story about Matt, he'll hate you," Kara countered, trying to rally.

"Oh," said Vera with a complacent smirk, "I wouldn't be that stupid. Do you think I'd write the story myself? All I have to do is drop a hint in the right ear and someone else will do it for me. You're the one Matt will blame, not me."

"But I'd let him know who was behind all the gossip."

Vera laughed. "He'd never believe you." Crushing out her cigarette, the redhead stood up and looked down at the tiny brunette. "Just think it over," was her parting shot as she turned and walked out, the sounds of her thin heels echoing on the hard floor.

Kara's mind was in a whirl. What could she do? she wondered in desperation.

Chapter Eleven

Kara huddled in the hard, plastic cafeteria chair. Vera's threat kept echoing in her mind. Had Matt confided in Vera about their marriage? It certainly sounded as if he had. And that meant Vera's statement must be true. He must have no real feeling for me, Kara told herself hopelessly. The reality of that was a crushing blow. In the back of her mind she had allowed herself to hope that Matt was beginning to care for her. It had been something she had clung to, she realized, in the face of all evidence to the contrary. But now there could be no more doubt. There was no reason even to hope.

She didn't know what to do next. What I need is someone to talk to, Kara told herself. Could she unburden herself to Uncle James? No. She dismissed the idea at once. Even though he was making good progress, he was still too sick to worry about her problems.

Well then, what about Matt's mother? Kara eliminated that option too. She needed someone who would be impartial. And Mrs. Jordan was too involved in the situation for that.

The only alternative was Jill. Perhaps she could go down to Georgetown and have a long talk with her old roommate. Maybe she could even stay with Jill, she reasoned. The idea lifted her spirits. It would be just like old times when they used to exchange girlish confidences into the wee hours of the morning. And, anyway, there was no way she could think clearly with Matt around, that was for sure.

Kara glanced at her watch. It was one o'clock. Matt would be at the hospital soon. She didn't want to meet him, didn't want to be confused by his magnetic virility.

After she had told her uncle she would be away for a few days, Kara hastily scribbled a note for Matt, explaining that she had to get away and think. She left it at the nurse's station, with instructions to deliver it to her husband when he arrived.

The ride from downtown Baltimore to Georgetown took almost two hours. And Kara's nerves were on edge when she parked her yellow hatchback in front of the red brick town house she shared with Jill.

Thank goodness I still have my key, she thought, as she opened the door and stepped into the small living room.

The room was dark. Kara realized Jill would still be at work. Maybe I'd better call Jill and warn her

I'm here, she thought. Picking up the phone, she dialed the office.

"Gee, Kara," her former roommate exclaimed. "It will be good to have you back for a while, even for a few days. But I've been roped into working overtime, so don't expect me until seven or so."

"Oh, that's all right," Kara reassured her, trying to keep the disappointment out of her voice. "We'll talk this evening."

Feeling somewhat at loose ends, Kara fixed herself a cup of tea, took off her shoes and lay down on the sofa to relax. Before she knew it, she had dozed off into an exhausted but fitful sleep. Her uncle's illness had taken a heavy toll on her reserves of energy. And the upsetting scene with Vera at the hospital had left her as limp as a wilted flower. Her emotions about Matt had never been more confused. And sleep was a welcome refuge.

She could have slept for hours there on the sofa. But after only thirty minutes, Kara was pulled back to dazed consciousness by a persistent rapping at the front door. Shaking her sleep fogged head to try and clear it, she pushed herself unsteadily to her feet. Who could it be? she wondered, swaying across the room toward the noise.

In her half-awake state, she neglected to put on the security chain. Before she knew what was happening, Wayne Lyle had stepped into the room.

"What, what do you want?" she asked uncertainly.

"Aren't you glad I'm here?" he inquired, his most charming smile plastered across his smoothly handsome face. "I was in the neighborhood and saw your car, so I thought I'd stop by."

"But I don't want to see you," Kara blurted. "I thought I made that perfectly clear at my wedding reception."

Wayne's expression became more serious. "You don't have to pretend anymore with me, Kara," he began. "I know all about your marriage of convenience. In fact, Vera and I have talked it over. It sounds as if you need a good lawyer, and I'm here to offer my services."

Kara's eyes narrowed. She hadn't even been aware that the two of them were acquainted. "How do you know Vera, and what business do you have talking to her about my marriage?" she challenged.

"Actually, we met at your lovely wedding reception," he explained, grinning broadly at her obvious surprise. "And we quickly found out that we had your and Matt's best interests at heart. Or I might rephrase that," he added meaningfully. "I'm interested in you, and Vera is interested in Matt."

Kara's face clouded. "You're presuming an awful lot, aren't you?" she asserted heatedly. "My relationship with Matt is no concern of yours or Vera's. But that's beside the point. I told you that I didn't want to see you again. And I meant it—under any conditions." She gazed at him levelly, intent on making her meaning absolutely clear.

The sandy-haired lawyer took a step forward. "You used to love me," he insisted, searching her uncompromising face intently. "I know you did. Everything was all right between us until you got involved with that posturing politician."

Kara found that she had involuntarily taken a step backward. In her heart she knew that her relationship with him had been over before she had met

Matt—even before Wayne had announced his affair with Gloria Ferguson. But there was nothing to be gained by bringing that incident up again, she reasoned. So she chose her words carefully. "No, you're wrong, Wayne," she corrected. "I might have been infatuated with you once. But now that I know what real love is, I can see the difference. I met you at a time in my life when I was vulnerable, when I needed affection. But things never could have worked out between us. We're just too different." Her violet eyes met his, pleading for him to understand. But neither her words nor her unspoken message seemed to be having the desired effect.

"You used to respond to my kisses," Wayne maintained stubbornly. "Let me prove to you that you will again." There was something in the young lawyer's eyes now that frightened Kara. Before his attitude had been conciliatory, almost pleading. Now there was a look of determination on his set features.

Kara shook her head and took another step backward. "Please leave, Wayne," she begged. "Please leave before you do something we'll both be sorry for."

But her words fell like stones against a brick wall. Paying no attention to her protest, Wayne closed the distance between them in a few strides and pulled her into his arms. As his lips descended on hers, she felt none of the excitement that Matt's lovemaking had aroused. And when Wayne tried to deepen the kiss, the feeling turned to one of revulsion. Desperately, Kara tried to turn her face to the side. And at the same time, she began to push against his chest.

She was so intent upon ending the embrace that she failed to hear the still unlocked front door open.

The next thing she knew Wayne's arms had been pulled roughly away from her body. And in a shocked blur she saw Matt knock the lawyer to the floor.

"I thought I told you to stay away from my wife," he rasped at the white-faced young man now sprawled in a daze on the rug.

The next thing Kara knew, Wayne had scrambled to his feet and made for the door.

"Oh, Matt, thank goodness you've come," Kara exclaimed. "I couldn't make him go away." But her relief at being rescued was cut short by the look of cold fury on her husband's face.

"It didn't look that way to me," he contradicted. "You didn't want me last night, but you couldn't wait to get down here to your old lover. When I got your note at the hospital, I knew this was where you would be."

"That isn't the way it was at all," Kara began, desperately smoothing her hair, her cheeks scarlet as her husband took in her disheveled appearance. But Matt gave her no chance to complete her protestation of innocence.

Reaching out and pulling her up against his taut body, he stared down into her flushed face, his features alive with emotion. Trembling, Kara caught the savage wildness in his eyes and tried to draw back. But his strong arms held her fast. She could feel his muscular thighs pressed hard against hers. And a tingling heat began to spread through her veins.

"Kara, you're driving me crazy," Matt murmured, pressing his lips against her hair. "I don't know what to expect of you from one moment to the next. But I know one thing, I'm going to make you forget about that two-bit lawyer."

Possessively, Matt began a deliberate attack on her senses. His lips trailed a path of fire across her cheek before settling warmly over her own. His hands slid down her back, molding the contour of her soft hips to his hard form. She could feel her body trembling in his arms. And when he cupped the fullness of her breasts, a soft moan escaped from her parted lips.

But despite her arousal, Kara struggled to resist him, trying to remember what the red-haired reporter had said only hours before. And then there were Matt's own actions. He had exploited her feelings for him in the past. Was he doing that now? But her body ignored the logic of her mind. It was impossible to resist him when she loved him so much. Without conscious thought, her arms slid around his neck, her fingers twining in the dark thickness of his hair.

With one hand, Matt reached down to the backs of Kara's legs, gently forcing them to bend. Then she felt herself being lowered to the red and blue oriental rug under their feet. In the next moment she felt the weight of Matt's body pressing urgently down on top of hers.

"Kara," Matt murmured. And his voice sent a wave of sensual anticipation to the core of her being. Sharp needles of desire pierced her. She felt Matt's fingers on the buttons of her blouse. In a moment he had removed the unwanted garment and unhooked the fastening at the front of her bra. His head bent to the soft mounds of her breasts, and his lips teased and caressed their sensitive peaks to aching tautness. She felt his hand trace the curve of her hip. And his lips were traveling upward to the warm hollow at the base of her neck, exploring her throat and shoulders in slow seductive movements.

Kara could hold nothing back in response. His hands and lips were melting all her inhibitions to a molten desire. With tender passion, she helped Matt out of his clothing, marveling at the sensuous feel of his bare skin against her hands, feeling the powerful ripple of his muscles. And when he took possession of her, she cried out at the all-consuming pleasure of their joining. It was as if she and Matt were being swept along on a powerful wave of passion that rolled and swelled and finally spent itself in ecstasy on some hidden beach known only to them.

Kara was overwhelmed with the intensity of her fulfillment.

"Oh, Matt, Matt, I love you," she whispered, pressing her cheek against his. But when she drew back to gaze into his face, Kara was brought up in sharp surprise. His eyes were dark with an expression she couldn't interpret.

"You can't really care about our marriage, or you wouldn't have come down here to Wayne," he forced out hoarsely. "I know I can make you respond physically. But I refuse to be a substitute for another man."

Kara's throat closed and she stared at him with horror, not knowing what to say. After the loving passion of her response, how could he believe such a thing? He must not have any real feeling for her, she thought brokenly.

In the next moment he had rolled away from her and begun to put on his clothes.

"No, Matt. Wait," she begged, thrusting her pride aside. "What we shared together, couldn't you tell it was something special—something I couldn't share with any other man?"

But he turned his head away, his face a hard mask as he pulled on his slacks. He had convicted her on circumstantial evidence. And she saw that he would not reverse his decision. Obviously he was seizing on the incident as an excuse to divorce her and marry Vera. He had cast her away with the ease of a broken campaign promise. When he left the apartment a few minutes later, he closed the door with a force that made the walls reverberate.

Sobbing, Kara struggled to her feet. She felt that she was standing on the edge of a precipice with the ground slipping out from under her.

"Oh, Matt, how could it have ended this way?" she cried to the empty room.

When he had slammed the door shut without another word, she knew he had slammed it shut on their marriage.

Kara looked wildly around the apartment. The tiny but elegantly furnished room that she had once loved was now a scene of emotional disaster for her. She couldn't bear to stay there any longer. Grief-stricken, she fled to the bedroom where some of her clothes still hung in the closet. Still sobbing, she pulled on a serviceable pair of slacks and an old blouse.

"I've got to get out of here," she murmured in desperation. "But where can I go?" Sinking down on the bed and cradling her forehead in her clenched hands, she tried to think clearly. She couldn't go to Uncle James's cabin. Too many memories of Matt waited there. Nor could she go to Matt's town house. That was impossible now.

Too distraught to make a rational decision, she abandoned the effort. "I just know I can't stay here any longer," she said aloud, wiping fresh tears from her cheeks.

Uncertain of her destination but determined to leave, Kara scribbled a hasty note to Jill, telling her not to worry. Then she snatched up her purse and headed out of the apartment. Once in her car she began to drive aimlessly, letting herself be swept along out of the city by the flow of rush-hour traffic. On the radio an announcer was talking about the imminent primary election. When she heard Matt's name mentioned, she hurriedly snapped it off.

She drove on in silence. And though she had no fixed destination in mind, an hour later she found herself on Route 97 heading north. She was only five miles from Windy Willow Farm.

Do I really want to go there? she asked herself. But then the warm, comforting face of Elizabeth Jordan surfaced in her mind.

She realized then that she desperately needed to turn to someone. And she had felt so at ease with this old friend of her own mother. Mrs. Jordan might be her mother-in-law, but she really seemed to care about Kara for herself, not just as her son's wife.

It was good to be able to make some sort of

decision. Ten minutes later she was heading up the curving drive to the now familiar stone house.

But after she had knocked on the door and stood waiting for someone to answer, a sudden panic gripped her. How could she explain any of this to Matt's mother?

Chapter Twelve

It was Mrs. Jordan herself who answered the door. And when she saw Kara's tear-streaked cheeks, she wrapped her arm protectively around the younger woman.

The gesture of compassion was more than Kara could bear. The floodgates of her emotional turmoil opened and she collapsed in tears on Mrs. Jordan's sympathetic shoulder.

"What is it? What's happened?" the older woman questioned anxiously.

But Kara could only shake her head, while she tried vainly to control her sobbing. Mrs. Jordan drew her into the family room, sat her down on the couch and waited for her emotional storm to subside.

When Kara was finally able to speak, she looked at her mother-in-law through tear-reddened eyes.

"I know it's all over between Matt and me," she

choked out. "I know for certain now that he doesn't love me."

Mrs. Jordan's blue eyes were full of concern. "Oh, Kara, I think you're mistaken. Would you like to tell me what happened," she continued in a gentle voice.

Kara shook her head. "Oh no. I just can't."

Wisely, the older woman didn't press her.

"Why don't you go upstairs and take a hot bath? And when you come out, I'll have a tray sent up to your room. Maybe you'll feel more like talking in the morning."

A hot bath. It sounded wonderful. She was halfway up the stairs when another thought entered her mind.

"Please, if Matt calls, don't tell him I'm here," she begged Mrs. Jordan.

The older woman hesitated. "But he might be worried about you."

Kara looked doubtful.

"All right, my dear, I'll respect your wishes for tonight."

Gratefully, Kara climbed the remaining steps and headed for the guest bedroom. Mrs. Jordan's voice floated after her. "Since you don't have any luggage, I'll leave a nightgown and robe in the guest room."

Alone at last in the bathroom, Kara began to run steamy water into the tub. Automatically she reached for a bottle of bath oil and poured it into the churning water. As the scent of peach blossoms rose to her nostrils, she remembered the similar bottle in Matt's apartment. Could it have been left there by his mother? But she didn't want to think of Matt just now.

Stripping off her clothes, she climbed into the tub

and sank down into the warm, scented water, letting it wrap her unhappy thoughts in an obscuring cloud of mist. She couldn't bear to think of what had happened. She wanted only to forget.

After her bath, she had a cup of soup and nibbled dutifully at the roast beef sandwich Mrs. Jordan sent her. But she soon set the tray aside and lay back against the soft pillows on the bed. Overcome by exhaustion it was only a few minutes before she had drifted off into a deep sleep.

Over the next few days, Mrs. Jordan was able to draw out some of the story that had brought Kara in such distress to Windy Willow Farm. She confided her doubts about Matt's love, her jealousy of Vera Caldwell, the cruel rebuff she had received from Frank Adams, and her feelings of inadequacy at being able to handle the job of a politician's wife. The stormy sexual encounters she kept to herself, not knowing what to say to Matt's mother about such intimate details of their marriage.

Tuesday was primary election day, and Kara stayed in bed late trying to avoid thinking about Matt. But when she finally came downstairs, a radio news broadcast describing voter turnout assailed her ears.

"I can see the election news distresses you," Mrs. Jordan said, setting down the cup of coffee she was drinking. Kara nodded weakly.

"You must realize that this primary is one of the most important days in Matt's life," the older woman continued. "His political future is at stake. It could be your future, too," Mrs. Jordan said pointedly.

Kara looked startled. For the past few days her

173

mother-in-law had been so comforting. But now her tone was firm.

"This is the time when Matt most needs you to stand by him. If you fail him now, how will you feel about yourself? After all, if you're honest, you'll admit that you do love him, regardless of your differences."

"But he doesn't love me," Kara objected. "And I can't take his rejection another time. He probably prefers Vera at his side now anyway."

"Is that what you really want?"

"Of course not," Kara admitted, realizing how true her statement was. She hated the thought of that redhead hanging on his arm. The idea made her sick.

"I never thought the daughter of Catherine Hilton Barnett would be a coward."

Kara blanched. "I'm not a coward!" she insisted.

"Then why are you admitting defeat without putting up a good fight?" Mrs. Jordan countered sternly.

"I . . . I don't know. I don't want to talk about it. I feel so confused. Let me think." Fleeing back to her room, Kara got dressed in a pair of jeans and a flannel shirt. Maybe the cool spring air outside would help clear away the fog of confusion that was clouding her mind.

She took a path that led away from the barn toward a small stream she could see in the distance. Its verge was snowy with massed bushes of blooming wild blackberries. As she absentmindedly plucked one of the blossoms and twirled it between her fingers, Mrs. Jordan's words echoed in her mind.

"A coward," she had called her. "A woman who

was willing to admit defeat without putting up a good fight." Maybe Mrs. Jordan was right. Maybe she was letting Vera win by default. She had faced Matt's rejection before. Maybe now she had to be brave enough to face it one more time—in order to win her husband back. She knew that she loved him and could never be happy with anyone else. Wasn't it worth any risk to make their marriage work?

Kara stopped in mid-stride, realizing she had made a decision. Resolutely she turned and hurried back to the house. Mrs. Jordan was still sitting at the dining room table and smiled when she saw the expression on Kara's face.

"You're right," her daughter-in-law announced. "Matt is worth fighting for. I'm going back to our town house now and I'll be by his side tonight when the election returns come in."

"I'm proud of you," Mrs. Jordan beamed. "I always knew you were a fighter. I only said those harsh words to make you realize it yourself."

Kara gave her mother-in-law a quick hug. "I'll see you at the election party tonight," she promised before running upstairs to get her purse.

Moments later she was in her car, heading for Matt's town house in Columbia. As she neared the entrance she wondered if he would be at home. But his car wasn't in the driveway. He must be out for a final campaign swing.

Inside, Kara changed into a flowered silk shirt-waist she had purchased at White Flint Mall. Then she carefully fixed her hair in a sophisticated up-sweep and meticulously applied her makeup. Her first stop was Matt's campaign headquarters in near-by Ellicott City, where she scooped up an armload of his literature. Although she hadn't been allowed to help with the campaign up till now, there was no way Frank Adams could stop her. Today she could do the same job as any campaign worker. Determined, she headed for the nearest polling place, where she spent the afternoon passing out flyers and talking about Matt to incoming voters.

She barely noticed when a TV camera crew appeared to record the voter turnout for the six o'clock news. Dinner was a doughnut and coffee brought in by one of the young campaign workers.

"When are you leaving for the victory party at the Kittamaqundi room?' the worker asked conversationally as Kara took a few moments out to eat.

She had been so caught up in campaigning that she had almost forgotten that she would be seeing Matt there that evening.

"I thought I'd wait till the polls closed," she told the worker.

He glanced at his watch. "Listen, it's already seven o'clock. Why don't you let me give out the rest of your literature and you go on over, Mrs. Jordan," he urged.

Kara smiled. "Thank you. I think I'll take you up on the offer."

But when she got in her car, a queasy feeling settled in the pit of her stomach. How would Matt receive her? Would she be able to carry through her role as politician's wife? Maybe if she went home and changed she could delay the moment of truth a little longer. But she vetoed the idea. If she went back to Matt's town house, she might not have the courage to show up at the reception at all.

Arriving at the stunning modern office building

whose top floor reception room had been reserved for Matt's election party, Kara eased her hatchback into a parking space. The building overlooked Columbia's downtown lake, and she glanced toward the serene blue water before pulling open the door to the lobby.

"I'm with the Jordan campaign," she told the sleekly coiffed receptionist.

"Oh, yes. You can go right up to the fourth floor."

"I'd like to stop in the powder room and freshen my makeup," Kara told her.

"Right around the corner," the woman gestured.

After patting a few loose strands of hair into place and putting on fresh lipstick, Kara drew in a nervous breath. It's now or never, she told herself and headed toward the elevator.

The elegant Kittamaqundi room with its floor to ceiling windows overlooking the lake was already half full. Kara searched the crowd for Matt. Finally she spotted him in a corner, head to head with Frank Adams. As she made her way toward them, Matt glanced up. A startled expression crossed his face. It was quickly replaced with a smile that didn't quite reach his steely eyes.

"Ah, here's Kara now," he said, giving her a searching look and drawing her to his side. "You will excuse us, won't you, Frank. We have a few personal matters to discuss."

Kara felt Matt's iron grip on her arm, as he led her to a small room at the side of the large hall. "Where in the hell have you been?" he rasped.

Kara blanched. "As a matter of fact, I've been at Windy Willow Farm," she countered.

"Do you expect me to believe that my own mother

wouldn't tell me where you were?" he snapped, his voice acid.

"I don't care what you believe; it's the truth," Kara insisted. This was not the reaction she had hoped for from Matt. Maybe she had made a mistake. Maybe she should never have come here at all. "Are you trying to make me leave?" she quavered.

But he shook his head, smiling cynically. "I didn't mean to give that impression, Kara. I don't know what your reasons are for showing up tonight. But I am grateful for small favors. And I certainly hope you're not going to run out on me again."

Kara mustered all of her dwindling stock of courage. "Matt, I've got to talk to you about why I came back," she began. But a loud knock on the door cut her short.

"Mr. Jordan, a reporter from one of the local TV stations is here. He wants to interview you right away."

Matt gave Kara a comprehending look. "You're right, we do have to talk. But we can't do it here or now. Can I count on you to stay this evening and see the election through?"

Unable to trust herself to speak, Kara nodded. She wasn't sure anymore what the two of them had to talk about; but now that she was here, she realized how bad it would look if she simply vanished again.

Kara followed Matt's disappearing form through the door back into the main room. Almost immediately one of the campaign workers stopped her.

"The first returns have started coming in," the woman announced.

"How's Matt doing?" Kara asked, trying at least to act the part of the proud politician's wife.

"It looks good," the woman assured her. "Matt's taken an early lead in the part of the district that we thought would be his weakest area."

Kara smiled. Despite her mixed feelings about Matt, she was pleased that he was doing well.

High expectations ran through the crowd. The reception was beginning to take on a definite party atmosphere. Someone pressed a glass of white wine into Kara's hand. And someone else handed her a plate with a corned beef sandwich. Not knowing how to manage both at the same time, she headed for one of the tables at the side of the room. Settling down, she saw that she was sitting next to the campaign worker she had met at the polls earlier that afternoon.

"After dessert, I see you've found the entrée," he joked as they were joined by Frank Adams.

"Hey, I saw you two on the six o'clock news," he said with the first trace of friendliness he'd shown toward Kara since they'd met. Looking surprised, the young woman nodded warily.

"If I'd known we were going to be on TV, I'd have worn a coat and tie," the worker kidded. It was just then that Matt appeared at the table.

"Were you campaigning for me this afternoon?" he questioned, giving Kara a quizzical look.

"Oh, she was there all afternoon, Mr. Jordan," the young worker answered for her. "She's quite a trouper. You're lucky to have her on your side."

Kara felt herself flush. And Matt looked puzzled. But before he could say anything else, a messenger appeared at his side.

"Telephone for you, Mr. Jordan."

Matt excused himself, and the little group broke up. Kara finished her sandwich and took a few sips of wine. I'd better not drink much of this, she thought. I'm so tired now it might just put me to sleep. Maybe I can get a cola at the bar.

She was on her way across the broad expanse of floor when Vera Caldwell, a fierce expression on her face, accosted her.

"I think we have something to discuss," she said pointedly.

"I don't have anything to discuss with you," Kara retorted.

"I think you do. And if you don't want to make a scene, I suggest you come out into the hall," the redhead insisted maliciously.

Feeling trapped, Kara allowed herself to be led out.

"What are *you* doing here?" Vera hissed when they were out of range of the partygoers.

"I have every right to be here at my husband's side," Kara parried.

"Even when you know your husband doesn't love you?"

Kara winced at the verbal thrust. But she remembered Mrs. Jordan's words.

"All I have is your word that Matt doesn't care for me," she countered. "And I'll have to hear it from *him* before I believe it."

Vera's face twisted in anger. "Why, the timid little mouse has claws. But they aren't long enough to scratch me. I suggest you crawl back in your hole before Wayne and I let loose a scandal that will really rock this city."

180

"But there's absolutely nothing between me and Wayne," Kara protested. "And there never will be. I can't stand the sight of him."

"Oh I don't doubt that," Vera soothed, "but I don't care what kind of story I have to use to get Matt away from your clutches. Admit it Kara, I'm a lot more suitable wife for Matt than you are."

Kara felt her knees turn to jelly. She had come here with such resolution. But she found herself no match for the redheaded reporter's vicious tongue.

She was casting around for a verbal weapon to hurl back when a harsh male voice intervened.

"Suppose you let the man in question pick his own partner," Matt suggested tersely as he stepped around the corner from the telephone room.

Vera gasped. But her recovery was almost instantaneous. "Why, Matt darling. We were just talking about you," she purred.

"I know you were," he replied evenly. "I heard most of it."

Coming up behind Kara, Matt put his strong arm protectively around her. "It seems to me, Vera, that your interest in my affairs has gone well beyond that of a reporter. And I would appreciate it if in the future you would restrict yourself to news coverage."

"I don't have to take that from you," Vera flung back. "I can ruin you, Matt Jordan."

For an answer he threw back his head and laughed. "I think you have a rather inflated opinion of your influence, Miss Caldwell. I have nothing to hide." Dismissing Vera with icy disdain, he turned his attention back to his wife. "I think we should go out and join the celebration."

Gently he propelled Kara down the hall, leaving the reporter clenching her fists.

As they neared the main room, Matt leaned over and murmured in Kara's ear, "I think I see things more clearly now—including the effects of Vera's lies." He looked down at his wife with a new warmth in his gray eyes. But before he could say more, a crowd of workers had swarmed around them.

"Quick, come over to the TV set. Bill Thorp is about to make his concession speech," someone shouted. Kara and Matt were swept along by a tide of well-wishers to the other side of the room.

The rest of the party was a blur of smiling faces, warm congratulations, popping flashbulbs and bubbling champagne. The only conversation she really remembered was a brief one with Matt's mother who had come to congratulate her son on his victory. After Mrs. Jordan had greeted Matt, she kissed and hugged Kara.

"Things seem to be working out the way you wanted, dear," she whispered, her blue eyes twinkling.

"Maybe you're right," Kara responded, daring to hope for the first time that there might be a way to straighten things out between her and Matt.

It wasn't until well after midnight that the young couple could make their escape from the room full of well-wishers and reporters.

"What about my car?" Kara asked in the parking lot.

"Oh, we'll get it later," her husband responded, putting his arm around her shoulder and guiding her toward the silver gray Porsche.

Once alone in the car with Matt, Kara felt suddenly nervous, wondering what to expect. And her feelings of anxiety intensified when Matt failed to say anything on the short drive home. Why was he so silent? What was he thinking about?

As they entered the foyer of the town house, the silence between them suddenly became unbearable. Kara put a tentative hand on her husband's arm. "Matt," she began, but the troubled look on his face brought back all her earlier doubts, and she didn't know how to break down the barrier.

"Let's go into the living room," he suggested at last. "We have to talk."

Apprehensively Kara sank down to the sofa. Matt joined her, sitting close enough for her to feel the overwhelming sensual awareness of his masculine presence even though he refrained from touching her.

From under fringed eyelashes, Kara studied her husband's finely chiseled profile. She could feel the tension within him—or was it just inside herself— she wondered fleetingly as he turned to look imploringly at her.

"Why did you come tonight, Kara?" Matt questioned intently as his strong hand took hers prisoner, keeping her from pulling away from his compelling gaze. He wasn't going to make this easy for her, Kara thought with dismay. He'd probably force her to confess her feelings for him then tell her that he was filing for a divorce.

"Your mother made me realize how important today is," Kara began uncertainly.

"So that's it," Matt said hoarsely, dropping her hands as a look of severe disappointment crossed his proud features. "You came out of a sense of duty," he added flatly. "You'll probably call me a fool. But Kara I'd hoped you had come back to me for another reason."

"And what other reason were you hoping for Matt?" Kara prompted gently, the quivering butterflies in her stomach making it difficult to breathe, much less talk.

Matt once again took her hands in his, and looked directly into her eyes. "You know I've been crazy with worry about you?" he began to explain, seemingly reluctant to answer her question directly. "I returned to your apartment that day—the day I behaved like a madman," he confessed. "When I had a chance to cool down, I was sick with shame over the way I'd treated you. And when you weren't there, I figured you'd left me for good."

Kara stared wordlessly at him for a moment. Then, seeing the anguish etched on his hard face, she found she couldn't doubt the sincerity of his words.

"I just had to get out of there," she explained in a low voice, unconsciously twisting her wedding ring on her cold finger. "I was sure after you left that you couldn't possibly love me."

"Not love you! But Kara, I've been crazy about you from the moment I first saw you in the firelight in your uncle's cabin."

Kara blushed when she thought of how she must have looked then, remembering their first stormy encounter.

"I knew then that I wanted you—that I would do anything to get you. I wouldn't have pushed you into marriage otherwise. Those reporters with your uncle did me a favor."

Kara gasped with surprise. "You mean you really did want to marry me?"

Matt looked a little shamefaced. "Well, what I wanted at the time was to get you into my arms—marriage seemed the only way. I spent the next few days wondering how I was going to follow through on my plans." Matt laughed briefly, his mouth twisting in an ironic grimace. Then he turned serious as he looked into Kara's questioning eyes. "It wasn't until I had to leave on that campaign trip that I realized what I really felt for you was love."

"Oh, Matt. That's when I knew too. And I felt so rejected when you left that night."

"Darling, you don't know how hard it was for me to leave you," he groaned, pulling her closer against him and nuzzling her neck with gentle lips.

"I thought of nothing but you all that week." He paused. "I can't say much for my behavior afterwards," he continued regretfully. "Seeing you in Wayne's arms and then your telling me you wanted an annulment—it was more than I could bear. I was consumed with jealousy and need for you. Where you're concerned I'm not quite rational."

Kara's heart pounded. "But, but what about Vera Caldwell?" she stammered.

"Kara, there was never anything between me and Vera. It was all in her mind. How could you believe that I could fall for someone like that?"

"And how could you believe that I would still be interested in Wayne after marrying you?" Kara countered.

Matt shook his head. "I was so afraid that I was going to lose you that I just wasn't thinking straight. But I realize now that if we had only known each other a little longer and had been able to talk to each other openly, we would have avoided a lot of misunderstandings."

Kara nodded in agreement. "And I guess it must have been Vera who clued in Wayne about our 'marriage of convenience.'"

Matt tightened his arms around his bride. For a moment they sat in silence as he stroked Kara's hair and brushed her forehead with his lips. Looking over in the corner, she saw the silver mylar balloon from Harborplace still floating—although it was now several feet from the ceiling. For a moment she was touched, but then an unwanted memory slid tauntingly into her mind.

"Matt, there's just one more question I have to ask you," she began hesitantly.

"Don't be afraid, Kara. We've got to base our marriage on trust of each other," her husband responded reassuringly.

"Well, what about that conversation I overheard between you and Frank Adams the morning after you had made love to me?"

Matt smiled ruefully. "Kara, I realized as soon as I saw you in the hall how it must have sounded. But you have to understand Frank Adams' point of view, too. You represented a terrible threat to all he'd worked for. First he couldn't believe I'd married someone he'd never even heard of. And then he was convinced that our marriage would cost me the election. I was trying to reassure him in a way that I thought he would understand. What I said to him had nothing to do with our lovemaking," he explained looking at her tenderly.

Kara felt her heart turn over. "Oh Matt, I love

186

you so much. I'm sorry I ever doubted you," she exclaimed, snuggling closer to the warmth of his embrace.

His lips brushed her hair. "Kara, I do love you so much," he murmured. "Winning your love means more to me than any election."

Kara's spirit soared. Then she heard her husband chuckle. "My room or yours?" he questioned.

"Ours," Kara responded dreamily as Matt swept her into his arms and carried her up the stairs.

Hours later, content in the fulfillment of their love, they held each other close in the large king-size bed.

"I have a week before I have to start campaigning again for the fall election. What do you say we take a honeymoon?" Matt suggested.

"I thought *this* was our honeymoon," Kara giggled.

"No, this was only the warmup. I have some influence with the owner of a romantic little cabin in the woods. Why don't we hide away there for a week," Matt told her.

"You've got my vote for that," she said as she reached out to stroke her husband's cheek. "But as long as we're together, it really doesn't matter where we are."

Silhouette Romance

15-Day Free Trial Offer
6 Silhouette Romances

6 Silhouette Romances, free for 15 days! We'll send you 6 new Silhouette Romances to keep for 15 days, absolutely free! If you decide not to keep them, send them back to us. You pay nothing.

Free Home Delivery. But if you enjoy them as much as we think you will, keep them by paying the invoice enclosed with your free trial shipment. We'll pay all shipping and handling charges. You get the convenience of Home Delivery and we pay the postage and handling charge each month.

Don't miss a copy. The Silhouette Book Club is the way to make sure you'll be able to receive every new romance we publish before they're sold out. There is no minimum number of books to buy and you can cancel at any time.

This offer expires April 30, 1983

Silhouette Book Club, Dept. SBU 17B
120 Brighton Road, Clifton, NJ 07012

    Please send me 6 Silhouette Romances to keep for 15 days, absolutely free. I understand I am not obligated to join the Silhouette Book Club unless I decide to keep them.

NAME_____

ADDRESS_____

CITY_____ STATE_____ ZIP_____

IT'S YOUR OWN SPECIAL TIME

Contemporary romances for today's women.
Each month, six very special love stories will be yours
from SILHOUETTE. Look for them wherever books are sold
or order now from the coupon below.

$1.50 each

Hampson	☐ 1	☐ 4	☐ 16	☐ 27	Browning	☐ 12	☐ 38	☐ 53	☐ 73
	☐ 28	☐ 52	☐ 94			☐ 93			
Stanford	☐ 6	☐ 25	☐ 35	☐ 46	Michaels	☐ 15	☐ 32	☐ 61	☐ 87
	☐ 58	☐ 88			John	☐ 17	☐ 34	☐ 57	☐ 85
Hastings	☐ 13	☐ 26			Beckman	☐ 8	☐ 37	☐ 54	☐ 96
Vitek	☐ 33	☐ 47	☐ 84		Wisdom	☐ 49	☐ 95		
Wildman	☐ 29	☐ 48			Halston	☐ 62	☐ 83		

☐ 5 Goforth	☐ 22 Stephens	☐ 50 Scott	☐ 81 Roberts
☐ 7 Lewis	☐ 23 Edwards	☐ 55 Ladame	☐ 82 Dailey
☐ 9 Wilson	☐ 24 Healy	☐ 56 Trent	☐ 86 Adams
☐ 10 Caine	☐ 30 Dixon	☐ 59 Vernon	☐ 89 James
☐ 11 Vernon	☐ 31 Halldorson	☐ 60 Hill	☐ 90 Major
☐ 14 Oliver	☐ 36 McKay	☐ 63 Brent	☐ 92 McKay
☐ 19 Thornton	☐ 39 Sinclair	☐ 71 Ripy	☐ 97 Clay
☐ 20 Fulford	☐ 43 Robb	☐ 76 Hardy	☐ 98 St. George
☐ 21 Richards	☐ 45 Carroll	☐ 78 Oliver	☐ 99 Camp

$1.75 each

Stanford	☐ 100	☐ 112	☐ 131		Browning	☐ 113	☐ 142	☐ 164	☐ 172
Hardy	☐ 101	☐ 130			Michaels	☐ 114	☐ 146		
Cork	☐ 103	☐ 148			Beckman	☐ 124	☐ 154		
Vitek	☐ 104	☐ 139	☐ 157	☐ 176	Roberts	☐ 127	☐ 143	☐ 163	
Dailey	☐ 106	☐ 118	☐ 153	☐ 177	Trent	☐ 110	☐ 161		
Bright	☐ 107	☐ 125			Wisdom	☐ 132	☐ 166		
Hampson	☐ 108	☐ 119	☐ 128	☐ 136	Hunter	☐ 137	☐ 167		
	☐ 147	☐ 151	☐ 155	☐ 160	Scott	☐ 117	☐ 169		
					Sinclair	☐ 123	☐ 174		

6 brand new Silhouette Special Editions yours for 15 days–Free!

For the reader who wants more…more story…more detail and description…more realism…and more romance…in paperback originals, 1/3 longer than our regular Silhouette Romances. Love lingers longer in new Silhouette Special Editions. Love weaves an intricate, provocative path in a third more pages than you have just enjoyed. It is love as you have always wanted it to be—and more —intriguingly depicted by your favorite Silhouette authors in the inimitable Silhouette style.

15-Day Free Trial Offer

We will send you 6 new Silhouette Special Editions to keep for 15 days absolutely free! If you decide not to keep them, send them back to us, you pay nothing. But if you enjoy them as much as we think you will, keep them and pay the invoice enclosed with your trial shipment. You will then automatically become a member of the Special Edition Book Club and receive 6 more romances every month. There is no minimum number of books to buy and you can cancel at any time.

Silhouette Romance

Coming next month from
Silhouette Romances

Another Eden by Anne Hampson

Richard was Susanne's world . . . but after the accident had
left her blind, it was his brother Nick at her hospital bedside,
opening up a brighter future than she ever imagined.

Loving Rescue by Dixie Browning

It was Lacy's first visit to Guatemala . . . her luggage and handbag stolen, was she also in danger of losing her heart to the
enigmatic Jordan Stone?

Make-Believe Bride by Nancy John

Would Belinda play substitute wife for Welsh farmer Adam
Lloyd when her scheming identical twin walked out on him and
Adam mistook her for his new bride?

Runaway Wife by Brenda Trent

When fashion designer Kati Autumn arrived in Mexico City, the
last person she expected to meet was Raul, her estranged
husband—who wanted her back again.

African Enchantment by Andrea Barry

Armand de Vincent was as exciting and dangerous as Africa
itself. How could Patricia be absolutely dedicated to her
dancing when she found herself so attracted to this playboy!

Mistletoe And Holly by Janet Dailey

Christmas festivities were the furthest thing from Leslie's mind
. . . until she met Tagg and found herself filled with a desire to
give the ultimate gift—her heart.